Erich K Ledermann MD FFHOM FRCPsych is a prominent and highly experienced medical doctor and psychiatrist who makes use of psychotherapy, homoeopathy and acupuncture, as well as conventional treatments, and has his own practice in Harley Street, London. He has written several books on natural health, and on medicine and philosophy, and been published in numerous journals.

By the same author

Existential Neurosis
Good Health through Natural Therapy
Mental Health and Human Conscience
Natural Therapy
Philosophy and Medicine
Your Health in Your Hands

MEDICINE

for the

WHOLE PERSON

———————————•———————————

A Critique of Scientific Medicine

ERICH K LEDERMANN
MD, FFHOM, FRCPsych

ELEMENT
Rockport, Massachusetts • Shaftesbury, Dorset
Melbourne, Victoria

First published in the USA in 1997 by
Element Books, Inc.
PO Box 830, Rockport, MA 01966

Published in Great Britain in 1997 by
Element Books Limited
Shaftesbury, Dorset SP7 8BP

Published in Australia in 1997 by
Element Books
and distributed by Penguin Australia Limited
487 Maroondah Highway, Ringwood, Victoria 3134

Cover design by Slatter Anderson
Page design by Roger Lightfoot
Typeset by WestKey Ltd, Falmouth, Cornwall
Printed and bound in the USA by Edwards Brothers, Inc.

British Library Cataloguing in Publication
data available

Library of Congress Cataloging in Publication
data available

ISBN 1-86204-056-7

Picture Credit
Figure 1 is reproduced by kind permission of The King's Fund, London.

CONTENTS

—————————————— • ——————————————

List of Figures   viii

Introduction   xi

PART I : SPIRITUAL HOLISM

1   THE REALM OF SPIRITUAL HOLISM   3

Spiritual Characteristics   3

The Ethics of Conscience   4

Social Spiritual Malaise   8

2   SELFHOOD AND THE SCIENCES OF THE MIND   22

Organic Psychiatry   22

The Psyche–Soma (Mind–Brain) Conundrum   24

Behaviour Therapy   26

The Cognitive Approach   28

Psychoanalysis   30

Jung's Analytical Psychology   35

Gestalt Encounter   38

Adler's Individual Psychology   39

3   SPIRITUAL CHALLENGES   43

The Threat of Anonymity   43

Guilt   45

Tacit Acceptance of the True-self Ethic   48

Tests Imposed by Illness and Death   48

4   A TRUE-SELF PSYCHOTHERAPY   57

Methods   57

Case Studies   61

Group Treatment   80

CONCLUSION OF PART I
Our Spiritual Existence   82

PART II: BIOLOGICAL HOLISM

5   INTERPRETATIONS OF BODILY WHOLENESS   87
    Bodily Challenges   87
    Machine-like Bodily Wholeness   88
    Biological Wholeness   89

6   NATURAL THERAPY   92
    Ecological Wholeness   92
    Physiological Wholeness   93
    Principles of Natural Therapy   99
    Applications of Natural Therapy   101
    Limitations of Natural Therapy   107
    Allies to Natural Therapy   108

7   EXAMPLES OF NATURAL TREATMENTS FOR THE WHOLE PERSON 113

8   HOLISTIC AND SCIENTIFIC MEDICINE   121
    Disenchantment and the Alternative   121
    Holism First, Science Second   127

PART III: SELFHOOD IN INTERPERSONAL RELATIONS

9   THE SELF AND THE OTHER   135

10 GUIDANCE FOR MARRIED AND UNMARRIED COUPLES   139
    Existential Counselling   139
    Scientific Systemic Counselling   140

11 GROUP PSYCHOTHERAPIES   143
    True-self Group Treatment   143
    Psychoanalytic Group Treatment   149

12 DOCTOR – PATIENT RELATIONSHIPS   154
    The Medical Clinician   154
    On the Other Side of the Fence   156
    Doctor: 'What Hat Should I Wear?'   157

13   LIBERATING MEDICINE   161

     Notes   167
     Index of Authors   179
     Index of Subjects   181

LIST OF FIGURES

1 'The Madonna and Child' by Sir Jacob Epstein
2 A patient's portrayal of herself as a gorgon
3 A patient paints herself in chains
4 The patient sees herself enmeshed in barbed wire
5 Fully recovered, the patient portrays herself in a happy hopeful situation
6 Recovery from facelessness
7 A patient portrays herself as a stunted tree
8 Correct posture showing the perfect alignment of the body
9 Incorrect and correct standing postures
10 Incorrect and correct postures for sitting in a chair and walking
11 An example of art used for discussion in group therapy

Dedicated
to my grandchildren,
to the younger generation

INTRODUCTION

———————————— • ————————————

This book is the result of many years of medical practice. The author lived through the epoch during which scientific medicine made enormous progress from which his patients benefited. But he realized that the scientific approach suffered from a fundamental weakness: individual unique persons were being treated as impersonal objects of science, as bearers of disease. Although efforts are made to educate people to avoid harmful habits such as smoking, taking excessive quantities of alcohol and eating excessive amounts of fat and sugar, people ignore this advice which is based on scientific evidence. Millions of people die of lung cancer due to smoking; of strokes and heart disease, which are the results of an unhealthy lifestyle.

Many people in the Western world have lost faith in scientific medicine and turn to such treatments as osteopathy, homoeopathy and acupuncture. The author added to his scientific qualifications those of homoeopathy and acupuncture, treatments which do not treat diseases but *whole people*. But such alternatives do not meet the fundamental need of taking responsibility for one's own health. This means accepting an ethic which does not call on people to seek such pleasure as indulging in unhealthy foods and drinks and in smoking, but which accepts obligations which are undertaken freely. This ethic became a fundamental principle in the author's psychotherapy, but, on a wider scale, it was the antidote to his patients' sense of despair and feeling that life was meaningless. This ethical freedom was recognized as a manifestation of people's spiritual dimension.

This spiritual holism (wholeness) forms the first part of this volume. It is a faith which is acceptable by all. It is denied by the sciences of the mind which are therefore held responsible for the moral confusion in today's society. This indictment is vindicated in the discussion of organic psychiatry, based on cerebral mechanisms, and of behaviour therapy, based on stimulus–response patterns. Libidinal psychoanalysis is held responsible for having distorted the human image by postulating a pleasure principle as the ultimate aim and aggressiveness as a primary instinct, as well as for having postulated a superego conscience which operates by extorting obedience, thus denying personal freedom.

Jung's analytic psychology is rejected as it denies the freedom and the obligation of responsibility, giving archetypal forces dominance. Gestalt therapy is not recognized because of its moral corruption and its confused picture of the human being. Finally, Adler's individual psychology is not accepted because of a doctrinal social interpretation. A tacit acceptance of a true-self spiritual ethic is postulated and illustrated by the courage of patients suffering from painful or terminal illnesses. The first part of the book ends by providing details of a true-self psychothcrapy, based on the acknowledgement of people's spiritual dimension.

The second part of the book looks at biological holism. It postulates the existence of an organic hierarchy which promotes the integration of the body's individual parts and biological functions, and also healing. Natural Therapy is based on the recognition of such forces and consists of advocating a lifestyle which avoids the harmful habits of over-eating, alcoholic excesses and smoking, and appeals to patients' ethical freedom to make their health their personal responsibility. Correct posture, judicious exercise, relaxation and exposure of the skin to water, air and sun play an important part. Homoeopathic medicine, acupuncture, massage, osteopathy and chiropractic are accepted as allies to Natural Therapy. They also rely on the wholemaking power of the organism.

The limitations of spiritual and biological holism are admitted. Patients suffering from severe mental illness may not be able to act according to a reliable conscience, as they may suffer from delusions and may experience guilt, but not as the result of immoral behaviour. Their false guilt may be a symptom, for instance, of severe depression. Bodily illness may not respond to holistic treatments, in which case patients must be given the benefit of scientific medicine when they will be made objects of science as anonymous bearers of a disease.

In the third part of the book, the true-self ethic is applied to human relations. This involves a critical appraisal of different schools of therapy and counselling. True selfhood means that people have to be aware of living in their own worlds but that they must welcome the others in their different worlds. The ethic is applied as group psychotherapy but such mutual respect is denied if counsellers accept self-fulfilment as the fundamental aim in life or if psychoanalysts apply their libidinal doctrine to groups of patients. The faults in the relationship between doctor and patient, conceived from a scientific academic point of view, are high-lighted, which provides an opportunity for a concluding chapter: a contrast between a supposed liberation of medicine, as envisaged by a representative of scientific medicine, and the liberation which is inspired by the ethic of spiritual freedom.

The issues raised in this book are clarified by reference to medical and philosophical literature and by case studies from holistic medical practice.[0]

Part I

---•---

SPIRITUAL HOLISM

1

THE REALM OF SPIRITUAL HOLISM

———————————— • ————————————

SPIRITUAL CHARACTERISTICS

What characterizes the realm of the spirit? It is the realm where people strive to achieve their potentialities as true selves. They are subject to the authority of their consciences, when they exercise their freedom to be persons in their own right, accepting conscience as an autonomous force which is not derived from social influences. It is the realm where people are credited with making responsible choices, when they dare to do so without always knowing the consequences and calculating the risks, where their selves transcend themselves. In that realm creativity is expressed in rhythmical movement, in music, in painting, in play, but where that creativity in not stifled by universal rules. It is the field where personal striving may be successful or it may end in failure to be followed by renewed effort, where people may climb out of the darkness of pessimism and nihilism into the light of faith. Then meaning is discovered in personal achievement which is based on personal freedom. There is no competition or subordination, however, for here people meet as equals.

Here people must bear the anxiety of insecurity and aloneness, must endure the despair and guilt of having failed when their strength has left them, but they can rejoice when the force of life returns, experienced as a miracle. Here unselfish love is born, and hate and resentment vanish. Here some find a relationship with their God and with their fellow beings, others with some nameless universal power, but all may find a foothold in their shaky world based on conscience.

This is the domain where science and technology and their mode of causality have no place, where people are not considered to be the result of biological, psychological or social forces, but where they are considered to be responsible for creating their own lives. Here freedom does not stand for licence nor for a person's ability to move his or her right arm or for any other bodily exercise. Ethical personal freedom is the key note and eminent thinkers have formulated what it stands for. Karl Jaspers, the psychiatrist and philosopher who was concerned with human existence, defined freedom as 'the *overcoming of the external*, which coerces me', but this external force is recognized as a force within because freedom 'comes into being where the other ceases to be alien to me, where rather I recognise myself in the other, or where the externally necessary becomes an element of my own existence, and is known and fashioned as such'. But Jaspers goes further: 'freedom is also the overcoming of *one's own arbitrariness*', which explains the assertion that 'freedom coincides with the inwardly present necessity of the true',[1] judged by conscience.

Martin Buber, Jewish philosopher, insisted that this is a twofold freedom, as a person may 'set at a distance not only his environment [the outer forces which affect everyone], but also himself [confronting the forces within him]'.[2] Buber's voice is heard again when he emphasizes the vital importance of the '*Thou*', a unique human person as distinct from an object – an '*It*' – and when he proclaims the truth: 'in all seriousness: without It man cannot live. But he who lives with It alone is not a man'.[3]

Goethe's advice that everyone should be prepared to die and to be reborn is heeded and everyone can identify with his Faust whose guilt (which he suffered as a result of deserting Margaret whom he had loved) is lifted when he receives the message: 'Pain and bliss have fled away; Thou art whole; let faith restore thee! Trust the new, the rising Day!'[4] But faith can be restored only to the person who for ever strives to achieve a true self.

According to a professor in the Department of Humanities in an American College of Medicine, the essence of spirituality is expressed 'most of all [in] the pursuit of meaning, and intimation of purpose and the sense of vital connection to one's ultimate environment [is] the dimension of depth in all life's endeavours and institutions'.[5]

THE ETHICS OF CONSCIENCE

The fundamental importance of ethical freedom as a means of healing the whole person was stressed in the Introduction. Its foundation lies in our conscience which tells us what is ethically right and wrong. The German philosopher F Heinemann has clarified the role that conscience plays in people's lives. Heinemann points out that our conscience preserves the moral equilibrium in our everyday lives, its voice provides the answer to a concrete situation which involves making a moral decision. The voice of conscience involves us in a dialogue. For example, it may say: 'You should or should not do that', or 'You should or should not have done that'. As Heinemann insists, even if we ignore this voice, it still is a compass that can direct us. He affirms the validity of this ethic, as conscience is 'implanted in our hearts'.

We can further agree with Heinemann that it does not matter whether we decide that conscience is innate or acquired, as long as it is awakened in children and continues to play its vital role throughout their lives. Our social life may shape the way our conscience instructs us, and our courts of law operate on the premise that we all, including the accused, have a conscience.

Heinemann draws our attention to the source that is responsible for the disastrous denial that conscience is autonomous, that it is derived from some other authority or from some scientific knowledge. The science of biology does not explain our conscience; we cannot blame our genes if we fail to act morally, nor should we excuse ourselves if our nervous system is too weak to bear the responsibility of our lives. It is true, however, that there are certain bodily diseases that interfere with the proper functioning of this 'compass' – for example, when we are in a fever, perhaps delirious or when we are suffering from some other condition that affects the normal activities of our bodies, such as an abnormal functioning of the thyroid gland. People suffering from severe mental illnesses, such as schizophrenia, which result in delusions and hallucinations obviously are unable to judge moral right. Severe so-called psychotic depression has the same effect. Such patients may declare that they have incurred a terrible guilt when, in fact, there is no objective justification for their feeling, which is merely a symptom of their illness. These guilty feelings disappear when they recover as the result of medication that affects their cerebral and, indirectly, their psychic-spiritual, ethical freedom. The same interference to the balance of the mind occurs when people are intoxicated, whether by alcohol or by an illicit drug. This does not mean, however, that their conscience does not urge them to give up such harmful habits and those who treat such patients rely on the stirring of conscience.

Heinemann also mentions the corruptive influence of psychological and scientific theory which we will discuss later. If a patient is told by his Freudian analyst that his Oedipus complex makes him feel guilty as he wanted to kill his father, the true-self therapist who has adopted the ethics of conscience will refuse to be drawn into this psychological moral corruption which has its source in a certain theory, based on an acknowledgement of the sexual instinct as an absolute basis for human life. Heinemann also quotes sociologists as the cause of moral confusion because they simply describe a state of society and are not concerned with the question of whether this state is morally right or wrong. Our present society suffers from such moral confusion, a spiritual malaise which will be highlighted in later sections of this book.

We have already postulated that conscience must be awakened in children while they are growing up and we fully agree with Heinemann that the ethic of conscience must be reawakened in our society which has to a large extent abandoned the principle which is interpreted in religious terms and ignored by the millions who have no religious faith. As conscience is interpreted in this book in general terms and not in any form of sectarian or spiritual-denominational ways, such awakening is possible and necessary. In the Introduction, the ethic which denies the fundamental ethical role of conscience is quoted; the seeking of pleasure and its psychological source is illuminated in the discussion on Freudian psychology which also provides an opportunity to expose the fallacy that conscience consists of the acceptance of parental or cultural authority and that it must only be accepted under threat. The awakening of conscience – the raising of an unconscious conscience into consciousness – is the main concern of this book.

An important question is 'how can people be motivated to adopt the ethic of conscience?' The answer lies in the fact that they must realize that their whole health depends on the acceptance of this ethic. Although philosophers of ethics deal with the duties which we owe to other people, the true-self therapist who aims at awakening the ethic of conscience in particular patients must take up not the unselfish ethical stance but a selfish one: 'what do I owe to myself?' is the question. The answer may mean that I owe to myself a fight for my moral independence, or that I have to resist my mother's, father's or any other person's domination. Their expression of love is false; it is possessive and thus deprives me of my own selfhood. But, as was affirmed by a quotation from Buber's *I and Thou*, the spiritual ethical relation to the other person is essential for attaining individual spiritual freedom. Therefore the ethics of conscience affirms the need to establish a relationship with the other person which is guided by considering his or her true selfhood. The whole of Part III of this book will be devoted to the question of selfhood in interpersonal relations.

Heinemann has drawn attention to the corruptive influence of others. As collective bodies – for instance, political parties or trade unions – they seduce the individual member to ignore what his personal conscience demands of him. The particular society expects loyalty from its members which may mean disloyalty to their true selves.[6] Moral conflicts which complicate the spiritual situation may have to be resolved by a person's conscience.

Jean-Paul Sartre has illustrated such a case. He recalled the dilemma of one of his students which occurred during the Nazi occupation of France. The young man was living with his elderly mother who completely depended on him. The question was whether he ought to leave her and join the Free French forces. Did he have a greater alliance and a greater responsibility to his mother or to his country? He argued: 'If I feel that I love my mother enough to sacrifice everything for her, my will to be avenged [on the Nazis], all my longings for action and adventure – then I stay with her. If, on the contrary, I feel that my love for her is not enough, I go.' But Sartre points out the flaw in this argument: 'How,' he asks, 'does one estimate the strength of a feeling?' The answer is that action must first be performed and that emotional appeal cannot justify an action in advance.[7]

There is no need to accept Sartre's conclusion that the man's choice, like all other people's choices, is not guided by any generally valid principle, and that people are thus 'abandoned' and suffer anguish. In fact, the student was guided by his conscience and he was bound to incur not anguish, but guilt, either by abandoning his mother or his country. He was thus sustained by a reliable universal spiritual force.

Moral conflicts are common. Doctors become involved in their patients' conflicting claims of spiritual moral rights – for instance, when pregnant women consider that they are entitled to have an unwanted pregnancy terminated. A doctor's conscience may not approve of abortions and he may refuse to meet the patient's demand. Another doctor may be found who has no such scruples.

Modern technological medicine has raised a number of spiritual problems. Should patients be kept alive artificially on life-support machines when the relatives are against such measures? Have patients who are terminally ill the right to die when they are in a life-threatening condition? Have patients who are suffering from incurable, painful illnesses the right to euthanasia? Have women the right to employ other women as surrogate mothers?

We will not discuss these problems as the various parties involved act according to what they consider to be the demands of their true selves. Rather, we will be concerned with those who accept their selves as objects of a cause-and-effect order, as losers of their spiritual true-self ethical freedom. One result of such misguidance is the large number of people who are suffering from mental illness because they have not understood

the fact that minds break down if the spirit is not accepted as the supreme
force in human lives.

SOCIAL SPIRITUAL MALAISE

MENTAL ILLNESS

A recent article in the *British Journal of Psychiatry* reveals an alarming
prevalence of neurotic illness and dependence on alcohol and drugs.
The figures confirm this book's thesis that we are dealing with a cultural
spiritual malaise which calls not for some scientific treatment, as this
would not be successful, but for a spiritual-ethical approach. The
statistics provide information about neurotic illness – to be defined later
– in England, Scotland and Wales, of people aged between 16 and 64
years of age: '14 per cent of these adults had a neurotic health problem,
women far more often than men.' This means that there are about
seven million sufferers. It is surprising that the authors of this article
consider as symptoms of a neurotic illness conditions which one usually
associates with everyday normal life problems. Now we have to
consider them as evidence of mental illness. 'The most common
neurotic symptoms were fatigue (27%), sleep problems (25%), irritability (22%) and worry (20%).' The diagnostic labels attached to these
symptoms are 'mixed anxiety and depressive disorder' (7.7%), followed
by 'generalized anxiety disorder' (3.1%).

We now learn that millions of people who feel weary and tire easily,
who cannot sleep, get irritable and worry a lot are suffering from illnesses,
defined as anxiety and depression. We must assume that most of these
patients are treated by drugs which influence their brains and frequently
lead to dependency and often serious side-effects, making their suffering
worse. These drugs never cure the neurotic disease, even if the anxiety
and depression is lessened temporarily. Many sufferers resort to alcohol
and incur a dependence which in the same article is rated as 4.7 per cent.
This occurs three times more often in men than in women, which means
that in Britain there are about two and a half million alcoholics.

The last item in this section of the article discusses drug dependence,
rated at 2.2 per cent: 'most prevalent among young adults, particularly
young men aged 16–24', about one and a quarter million sufferers.[8] Drug
addiction will be dealt with in the next section.

The picture of society's spiritual malaise is even more disturbing when
we consider recent information on children who were not included in

the article. The figures were published by the Medical Research Council in conjunction with The Institute of Psychiatry, and were reported in a recent issue of *Mims Magazine Weekly*. These were the findings:

> Almost a quarter of children attending GP surgeries have severe mental health problems, but only 2 per cent are identified by GPs. Two million suffer from mental ill health, half of whom have moderate to severe problems. Adolescents aged 14–15 are three times as likely to have emotional and conduct disorders as those aged 10–11 . . . There is a clear link between mental health problems in parents and in their children . . . The risk of mental illness increases in families where the parents are unemployed, divorced, living alone or are homeless.[9]

In a book published in 1995 entitled *So Young, So Sad, So Listen,* the authors found that 'depression is one of the most common serious problems in today's school-age population, teenagers from 5 to 16'.[10] Clearly, these children and their families are suffering from a spiritual malaise which affects their society, although economic factors also play a part.

DRUG ADDICTION

These are the drugs used by addicts and their effects.

Marijuana   There may be an effect on the heart, the blood vessels and the lungs, while memory, intellect and cognition may be impaired. Sensory and perceptual functions and concentration may be disturbed. Some addicts become fearful, confused, excessively dependent, aggressive, panicky and may even suffer from hallucinations and distortions of their body image. If they also suffer from schizophrenia or manic-depressive illness, these conditions are liable to get worse. Marijuana is often combined with substances which cause more serious addictive symptoms and with alcohol. It is taken by many millions of people, mostly the young.

Cocaine   This drug quickly creates psychological dependency and strong craving. It ruins a person's social life as the results include anxiety and hallucinations of touch, taste and smell. There is constriction of the blood vessels, a rise in body temperature, in heart rate and blood pressure. People are tempted to take cocaine as it produces an immediate feeling of well-being and confidence. Its abuse is spreading rapidly in America and is threatening to become more popular in Europe.

Heroin   This drug relieves pain and, like cocaine, provides a feeling of well-being. A most powerful dependency develops. The withdrawal symptoms include shaking, sweating, vomiting, muscular pain, abdominal cramps, diarrhoea and weakness. Addicts experience flushing, palpitations and pain in their arms, legs and back.

An article in *The Listener* provides an insight into the heroin situation and in the financial gains which people make: a poppy grower may sell his/her crop for £30. When converted into heroin and transported to Britain, the same quantity fetches £700, an increase of about 2,000 per cent. The pushers who receive the drug, usually addicts themselves, have to make a profit when selling heroin. One of the pusher-addicts was interviewed and gave the following account:

> One of the main effects is weight loss, you completely lose your appetite. At the moment I've got an extremely bad chest. I feel as though I've just run up the stairs, wheezing and out of breath. And you're for ever coughing up phlegm. As for sex, it just goes out of the window once you're into heroin . . . Heroin rots your teeth, it kills you generally.

Another addict continued:

> All you seem to need to get you through the day is your heroin. First thing you think of in the morning and the last thing you think of at night is your heroin. There are also changes in your personality . . . I mean, I'd do things for money [to buy heroin] that I would never have dreamt of doing – stealing, shoplifting, burglary, anything, it doesn't matter what it is. You'll even rob your mother and father . . . Then there's the lying. Your whole life's a lie. From the time you wake up in the morning until you go to bed you are just telling one lie after another to con people, to get money. Heroin completely changes a person to a totally different person, a bad person.

When this pusher-addict was asked how people whose children he corrupts feel about him, he admitted that he may be beaten up or abused by them. So the interviewer asked: 'Aren't you killing their sons and daughters?' and the answer was: 'Yes, I suppose I am.' But another pusher-addict interrupted: 'No, they're killing themselves' and when asked: 'Do you feel guilty selling heroin [to people]?', the reply was: 'I always feel guilty . . . I sell heroin because if I didn't do this, I'd be out robbing. I don't want to rob any more because I don't want to go to prison again.' The interview ended by revealing the tragic mistake made by the novice: 'People think that they'll never get addicted. Everybody they know is addicted to heroin and they'll sit down, smoke it and they'll honestly believe that they won't get addicted. They might not for as long as a year, but, in the end, they'll be smoking it every day and [they are] not able to stop.'[11]

The addicts' admission of guilt confirms their recognition of the spiritual dimension. Unfortunately, its force may not be strong enough to allow addicts to give up the drug which has such a powerful hold over them; other addicts suffer from the same weakness. The case illustrates the vulnerability of the spirit.

The Stages of Hard-drug Addiction

An American author has called drug addiction a 'progressive disease'. He has traced the stages through which the young addict passes. He called stage 1 'learning the mood swing'. Children are prepared for drug abuse as they grow up in a world where there is 'a drug relief for every problem, from minor aches and pains to night cough and tired blood'. The same author maintains that 'television, magazines, movies, and music have strongly influenced the popularization of marijuana, alcohol, and tobacco and have contributed to their wide use and fashionable acceptance'. Young people are introduced to drugs by their friends, they enjoy the feeling of being high, of the excitement, of the new sense of belonging. In the first stage there may not be any behavioural changes except for covering up the illicit activities.

Stage 2 is called 'seeking the mood swing'. Now the addict 'smokes pot to relax for an algebra test, or to deal with the discomfort of obesity, acne, a demanding father, or being turned down for a date'. School performances suffer. The moral sense deteriorates, while responsibilities are no longer accepted. The young person becomes irritable, as he or she is trapped in drug abuse.

Stage 3 is characterized by 'preoccupation with the mood swing'. The patient is now hooked on hard drugs and needs money to get hold of them. His search for well-being becomes bizarre. As the need for drugs increases, so the addict turns into a delinquent.

The fourth stage is known as 'doing drugs to feel OK'. With a growing need for even larger quantities of drugs, bodily illness develops, the addict drops out of school or work, and family life becomes non-existent. Crime and a social and mental breakdown is the final outcome. The person's freedom and moral sense are gradually eroded.[12]

Other Mood-changing Drugs

Inhalants   When sniffed, intoxicants such as glue affect the central nervous system, which in turn affects consciousness. They cause a feeling of well-being, excitement, loss of inhibition, dizziness, loss of memory and the inability to concentrate. They impair judgement, cause recklessness and produce a feeling of omnipotence. Delusions and hallucinations may occur, and the heart may be damaged. The users are often children or adolescents.

Analgesics (painkillers)   America, Britain, Australia, Denmark, Switzerland and Sweden are all countries in which painkillers are used in large quantities by people to achieve temporary intoxication, and to feel invigorated and stimulated, thus improving their performance. These addicts frequently combine analgesics with alcohol or drugs that affect their mood. They are often diagnosed as suffering from psychiatric disorders. This form of drug abuse damages the kidneys and the stomach, it can cause anaemia and blood disorders, it harms the nervous system and gives rise to headaches. As these substances are sold over the counter, millions of people make illicit use of them.

Amphetamine ('speed')   This stimulant makes people mentally and physically more active, but there may also be anxiety, and nervous and physical tension, especially with large doses. People may start to tremble, get confused and feel giddy. They may also suffer from palpitations which increase their feeling of alarm. Severe emotional dependence follows. The addict may show signs of serious mental illness; tolerance develops, which means that larger amounts of the drug are needed to provide the same stimulating effect that was first experienced. Because doctors have practically ceased to prescribe amphetamine, addicts obtain this drug from those who manufacture it illicitly. But there are a number of mood-changing drugs which lead to dependency and which people obtain through their doctors' prescriptions. Many such drugs are given to calm people down or to help them to sleep.

Barbiturates   These act as sedatives and hypnotics, impairing intellectual functions and judgement. Elation of mood and decreased motor activity may occur. Time seems to 'fly'. Addicts obtain barbiturates illicitly. Mild tranquillizers of the valium type (*benzodiazepines*), on the other hand, are prescribed in their millions to patients to relieve anxiety, tension and agitation, and to induce sleep (for which milder drugs of the same type are prescribed). It has become clear that severe dependency is liable to develop and doctors are now advised to avoid using these powerful agents to calm people down for long periods. Many people however, have taken these substances habitually and experience the greatest difficulty in breaking the habit.

LSD (lysergic acid diethylamide)   This drug causes visual hallucinations, objects appear distorted, time may seem to stop or to pass slowly, or it may even get faster and faster. People may feel relaxed and happy, but they may also become fearful and depressed. Addicts may feel that they have lost their personality and a dreamy state supervenes. The heart beat accelerates, some people become mentally unstable and suicidal. Even after the effects have worn off, they may suddenly reappear. Although people do not develop drug dependency on LSD, many feel the urge to repeat their 'trip'.

The Psychology of Drug Addiction

Psychologists have studied drug addiction. One author has summarized his findings which are concerned with adolescents. Their personalities show 'rebelliousness, autonomy strivings, liberalism, willingness to try new experiences and striving for independence. The behaviour and attitudes of peers and friends play a large part in seducing young people to become addicts'.[13]

Other writers conclude that sensation-seeking characterizes those who are addicted to a variety of drugs.[14]

In a further paper the question is asked: what motivates such a vast number of people to use such harmful substances? The following answers are given: those who take marijuana do so 'to help with feelings of stress, anger, depression, frustration and boredom . . . to reduce feelings of loneliness and isolation, to enhance creativity and productiveness, to increase social and sexual effectiveness, to fill a moral and spiritual void'. When the background of young addicts was investigated in America,

> a vast body of research has shown that the absence of a parent through death, divorce, or a time-demanding job contributes to many forms of emotional disorder, especially anger, rebelliousness, low self-esteem, and anti-social behaviour that characterize drug users . . . over half the children under the age of 18 (approximately 13 million) live in a home with one or both parents missing.[15]

These young vulnerable people fall easy victims to the ruthless multi-million pound criminal organization that makes enormous profits from dealing in drugs. But these findings do not explain the tragic situation; they do not tell why young people today express their rebelliousness, striving for autonomy, freedom, new experiences or sensations, by using such harmful substances.

Thomas Szasz, an American psychiatrist, maintains that in the drug addict 'the desire for the drug is experienced as issuing from the very depth of the user', and he concludes that 'it is precisely this experience of an inner need of "craving" that justifies our placing this behaviour in the same class with other patterns of religious conduct and observance'. He finds the common denominator for drug taking and religious experience in 'a profound inner desire or urge, whose satisfaction gratifies the user's deepest sense of existence or being in the world'. Szasz may be correct in assuming that drug taking fulfils 'a profound inner desire or urge', but he is surely not correct that this is the same urge which is at the root of a religious experience. Szasz holds that the addict is convinced that 'only with the drug is he "whole" ', and that, of course, does apply to the religious person who feels 'whole' only in communion with God. According to Szasz, the drug experience is sought as a 'contrast' to the 'universal human experience of helplessness and powerlessness and of being manipulated by external agents and their hostile interests'.[16]

The inner urge 'whose satisfaction gratifies the user's deepest sense of existence or being in the world' is a spiritual urge. For those who cannot gain such satisfaction in religious experience, the alternative is to discover their own authority in their conscience, which means that they are no more 'being manipulated by external agents and their hostile interests', but that they impose their own authority upon themselves. Thus they achieve wholeness without the aid of a drug. They become creative and productive; their striving for autonomy is fulfilled; they are neither bored nor frustrated, isolated and lonely; they are not angry, rebellious, suffering from low self-esteem, or behaving in an anti-social manner. They also gain independence from those who try to seduce them to become addicts. They have filled the 'moral and spiritual void' in which they were placed by their parents' failure to provide a secure environment in which they would have grown up loved and acknowledged.

Drug addicts may save themselves by accepting a true-self ethic which is a manifestation of spiritual holism, but they cannot be saved by the science of medicine or psychology. The same limitations of science apply to those victims of the social malaise who decide to commit suicide or who inflict harm on themselves.

SUICIDE

The suicide of adolescents is the third leading cause of death among young people in America. As with drug addiction, the role of the family plays a major part: 'Suicidal youths experience greater family disorganization than non-suicidal youths . . . youthful suicidal behaviour may be associated with an inability to achieve adequate family relationships'.[17] Family disorganization affects adversely all the members of the family and is responsible for the conflicts which make people indifferent to bodily and mental health. Parental discord has harmful effects that go beyond the age of childhood and adolescence. Attempted suicide in adult life has been related to traumatic experience in early life.[18]

The loss of a parent, whether by divorce, separation, desertion or death, induces self-blame in the child and a desire for reunion with the parent. It 'predisposes to depression and suicidal behaviour later in life'.[19]

Parental suicide makes children vulnerable to psychological disturbances.[20] Not only does their mental health suffer but serious problems of bodily health affect all the members of a family which has experienced the trauma of an attempted or threatened suicide.[21]

Housing and economic factors are important: youthful suicide is related to overcrowded living conditions, while unemployment and debt also play a part.[22] A cultural influence is marked: a particularly high suicide rate occurs among adolescents in Japan where traditionally suicide is considered to be honourable. However, the number of young Japanese who commit suicide has decreased, although suicide among Japanese aged sixty-five years and above is still one of the highest in the world of this age group. This is because the older generation have not changed their views as the result of contact with the West, unlike the younger members of the community.[23]

There is a link between suicide and drug addiction. Youthful heroin addicts and male alcoholics attempt suicide more frequently than people who are not so addicted.[24] One writer who has examined the aetiology and treatment of young people's attempted suicides holds that 'some adolescents are so emotionally bankrupt, particularly the chronic drug abusers or alcoholics, that they have no significant objects in their lives. This may be a particular issue if they have been involved in drug dealing, because drug dealers alienate others in their role as exploiters. In addition, their family and friends are often angry and alienated. Their survival then seems to themselves quite irrelevant to others. As a result, these individuals may become highly suicidal and will require hospitalization.'[25]

In Britain, suicide among the under-45-year group is the second commonest cause of death, accounting for 10 per cent of all potential years of life lost. The study reveals a dramatic increase in suicide among young men, especially security force personnel.[26]

Norway has experienced a great increase in the number of suicides. Even Norway's remarkably low unemployment rate (3 per cent) has not prevented a sevenfold increase in the number of young people committing suicide over the past two decades. Professor Nils Johan Lavik of the psychiatric clinic in Oslo attributes this trend to an 'internal turmoil' of the people, although the country is 'superficially well-ordered and afflu-ent'. He argues that there may be an indirect connection between the oil bonanza and suicide: oil gave the momentum to internal migration which, in turn, helped to loosen the social network of small communities in which family and religion gave substance to many individual lives. He further points out that those who are not able to benefit from the technology feel isolated, especially in Oslo where the number of suicides is especially high and often carried out under the influence of drink and drugs by young people 'who become desperate when they find that their high expectations of life cannot be fulfilled'.[27] By 1988 the figure had risen to 27.9 per 100,000 population.[28] The highest increase among men has occurred in the group aged 15–29 years in the northern part of the country, and for women in the group aged over 30 years in rural areas.[29]

Deliberate Self-harm

When somebody has attempted suicide, there is a definite chance that such a person will eventually succeed in ending his or her life. This is evident from a Scandinavian report: compared with the suicidal risk of the total population in Helsinki, this risk was increased 50 times among the 1,018 self-poisoned patients who had been treated in the emergency room of Helsinki University Central Hospital.[30]

In Great Britain, deliberate self-poisoning remains the most common reason for acute medical admission in young people. Many of them have no desire to kill themselves at the time of harming themselves. Their usual motives are their desperate wish to communicate their plight to the world around them and to gain relief from their intolerable distress. As in Helsinki, many of these young people finally commit suicide by taking a drug overdose.

The social malaise of self-inflicted harm is not only evident in the vast numbers of mentally ill people, but in the numbers of drug addicts, suicides and those who overdose on drugs. This malaise is also evident in the staggering number of people who contract venereal diseases, especially AIDS (acquired immunodeficient syndrome).

AIDS

Although most drug addicts acquire AIDS by using infected needles and although some haemophiliacs have been infected as a result of blood transfusions, most victims contract the virus through sexual intercourse (babies born of infected pregnant women are the exception). The symptoms may take years to manifest. As the immune system is affected, patients suffer from a wide variety of symptoms of the disease which is incurable and which can only be palliated by the use of expensive drugs. There is no medical prevention.

An official report quotes the following figures of the extent of the spread of the infection:

> In mid-July 1996, an estimated 21.8 million adults and children worldwide were living with HIV/AIDS, of whom 20.4 million (94 per cent) were in the developing world. Close to 19 million adults and children (86 per cent of the world total) were living with HIV/AIDS in sub-Saharan Africa, and in South and Southeast Asia. Of the adults, 12.2 million (58 per cent) were male and 8.8 million were female. Worldwide during 1995, 2.7 million new adult HIV infections occurred (averaging more than 7,000 new infections each day). Of these, about 1 million (an average of nearly 3,000 new infections per day) occurred in Southeast Asia and 1.4 million infections (close to 4,000 new infections per day) were in sub-Saharan Africa. The industrialized world accounted for about 55,000 new HIV infections in 1995 (nearly 150 new infections per day; about 2 per cent of the global total). In 1995 approximately 500,000 children were born with HIV infection (about 1,400 per day); of these children 67 per cent were in sub-Saharan Africa, 30 per cent in South and Southeast Asia, and 2 to 3 per cent in Latin America and the Caribbean.
>
> From the beginning of the pandemic until mid-1996, an estimated 27.9 million people worldwide have been infected with HIV. The largest numbers of HIV-infected individuals were in sub-Saharan Africa, totalling 19 million (68 per cent of the global total), and in South and Southeast Asia, totalling 5 million (18 per cent of the global total).
>
> Since the beginning of the pandemic, the majority of HIV infections – 26 million (93 per cent) – have occurred in the developing world. The number of HIV-infected people in South and Southeast Asia is now more than twice the total number of infected people in the entire industrialized world.
>
> The global cumulative number of HIV infections among adults has more than doubled since the beginning of the decade, from about 10 million in 1990 to 25.5 million by mid-1996. Of these, 14.9 million were men (58 per cent) and 10.5 million were women (42 per cent).

The same report also gives information on how many carriers of the virus have developed the feared disease with all its deadly complications:

> More than 6 million adults have developed AIDS from the beginning of the pandemic to July 1996, and of these 4.5 million (close to 75 per cent) were in sub-Saharan Africa; 0.4 million were in Latin America and the Caribbean (7 per cent); and 0.75 million were in North America, Europe and North and South Pacific (12 per cent). In South and Southeast Asia where the pandemic

gained intensity more recently, it is estimated that 0.33 million adults have developed AIDS. Of the 1.6 million children with AIDS, the majority – 1.4 million (85 per cent) – were in sub-Saharan Africa.[31]

These figures spell disaster for many communities and represent a vast dimension regarding the current social malaise. Of course, they are a manifestation of the powerful sexual instinct. Different cultures have different sexual behaviours. Medical authorities advocate for all the use of condoms which can prevent AIDS, other venereal diseases and unwanted pregnancies. But in our civilization far more is required – an acceptance of the spiritual dimension which values love as its most precious ingredient.

Erich Fromm, who studied sociology and psychology and who was trained in psychoanalysis, has in his writings tried to awaken people, alienated as they are from each other in today's society, to their true selves. As Fromm points out:

> love is not the result of adequate sexual satisfaction, but sexual happiness – even the knowledge of the so-called sexual techniques – is the result of love. If the desire for physical union is not stimulated by love . . . it never leads to union in more than an orgiastic, transitory sense . . . Sexual attraction creates, for the moment, the illusion of union, yet without love this 'union' leaves strangers as far apart as they were before – sometimes it makes them ashamed of each other, or even makes them hate each other, because when the illusion has gone they feel their estrangement even more markedly than before.[32]

Sexual permissiveness conflicts with the spiritual ethic of love. It expresses people's overwhelming sexual desires and their conviction that they are entitled to such pleasures in relationships that are devoid of love. In their attitude they are influenced by the society in which they live. But they may pay the price of unwanted pregnancies, and painful and dangerous venereal diseases, including AIDS. They may find the price too high. Even if they protect themselves with the aid of condoms, they may feel guilty that they have been unfaithful to their true selves, and they are left emotionally unfulfilled. Sexual permissiveness must be understood in a wider context, one which is concerned with values that are held by society. A crisis in valuation is an important factor in the explanation of modern society's malaise.

CRISIS IN VALUATION

The sociologist Karl Mannheim wrote his book *Diagnosis of Our Time* during the Second World War.[33] In the second chapter, entitled 'The Crisis in Valuation', the author holds that:

in a society where disintegration has proceeded too far, the paradoxical situation arises that education, social work and propaganda, notwithstanding highly improved techniques, become less and less efficient because all the values that could guide them [the people] tend to evaporate. What is the use of developing exceedingly skilful methods of propaganda and suggestion, new techniques of learning and habit-making, of conditioning, de-conditioning and re-conditioning, if we do not know what they are for? What is the good of developing child guidance, psychiatric social work and psychotherapy if the one who is to guide is left without standards? Sooner or later everyone becomes neurotic, as it gradually becomes impossible to make a reasonable choice in the chaos of competing and unreconciled valuations.[34]

Mannheim considers these 'unreconciled valuations' to be the result of the uncontrolled and rapid growth of modern society which interferes with the exercise of personal human relations built on love and concern for everyone and due to the complexity of industrial society which exploits its workers and no longer requires the skills and craftsmanship of the pre-industrial era. Mannheim cites as further destabilizing factors collective responsibility in place of prestige with regards to working incentives and the loss of self-respect because people are unable to take responsibility in the workplace; and the loss of influence that political and religious leaders once held.

The American sociologist Richard Sennett has drawn attention to the detrimental effects of fundamental changes in modern society. They lead to the replacement of a person's authentic self by the 'protean self' which has no core of innateness, but is 'a creature of immediate appearances and sensations'. This selfhood puts an immense premium on 'direct' experiences with other people; it detests reserve or masks behind which other people are felt to lurk, because in being distant they seem to be inauthentic. In dedicating oneself so thoroughly to a sensate, direct life of experience, one cannot make long-term commitments. In the realm of sexuality, this belief in a protean self suggests to people that 'who' they are depends on who their lovers are and how much they experience in love. This code [of the protean self] treats intimate interchanges as a market of self-revelations. You interact with others according to how much you tell them about yourself: the more 'intimate' you become, the more confessions you have made. When the partners run out of self-revelations, the relationship all too often comes to an end; there is nothing more to say, and each takes the other for granted.[35]

Sennett's observations provide a clue to the understanding of society's malaise: people have lost their true selves and the protean self is false, so people's values are also false. Their dedication to 'a sensate, direct life of experience' leads to drug addiction with all the disastrous consequences. Their unstable selves can only make unstable human relationships. This crisis can be resolved only if people accept an ethic which enables them to recapture their true selves.

At a conference concerned with human values, the well-known biologist Ludwig von Bertalanffy linked the social malaise and its consequence for mental health to a breakdown in people's 'symbolic universes in language, thought, and all other forms of behaviour'.[36] As symbols stand for what people believe in, what makes their lives meaningful, so the breakdown in a person's mental health spells out nihilism. Von Bertalanffy illustrates his thesis as follows:

> the economic symbol of money has lost its connection with reality, a banknote does not represent any more a fixed quantity of gold or of commodities but is subject to continuous re-valuation, to inflation, sometimes at an astronomical scale, and other machinations. Art used to be a symbol-system representative of a certain period in a certain culture. Today's 'art' seems to extend from the finger-painting of a chimpanzee recently reproduced in *Life* magazine and presenting a good example of modern nonrepresentative pictures to the homey covers of the *Saturday Evening Post*. Even the symbolic universe of science, which is about the only solid thing we have, is shaky in certain aspects and places. The same symbol, democracy, means exactly the opposite when uttered in the West or in the Communist world. The symbolic system of religion which, abstracting from its intrinsic values, at any rate has developed organically in the long course of history, is supplanted by kaleidoscopically changing pseudo-religions, be they scientific progress, psychoanalysis, nationalism, soap opera or tranquilizers . . . The modern methods of propaganda, from the advertisement of a tooth paste to that of political programs and systems, do not appeal to rationality in man but rather force upon him certain ways of behavior by means of a continuous repetition of stimuli coupled with emotional rewards or punishments. This method is essentially the same as that applied to Pavlovian dogs when they were drilled to respond to a meaningless stimulus with reactions prescribed by the experimenter . . . No wonder, then, that the breakdown of the symbolic universe leads to the experience of being lost in a meaningless world.

The writer concludes that for those who 'lack sophistication, there are two other outlets: crime and mental disease. Juvenile delinquency reaching a peak under optimum economic conditions – what else can it mean than the practice of a philosophy of meaninglessness?' Then follows the confirmation that a great deal of mental illness is a symptom of a spiritual social malaise, of a loss of values: 'and there is that other outlet – mental ailment to the tune of some 10 million cases in the United States, or the

52 per cent mental cases of all hospitalized patients'. He denies that stress is the cause of mental derangement. The true explanation is that 'When life becomes intolerably dull, void, and meaningless – what can a person do but develop a neurosis?' The experiment in which people are deprived of incoming stimuli (which corresponds to a deprivation arising from their essential symbolic universe) is cited; the result is 'a model psychosis with intolerable anxiety, hallucinations, and the rest'.[37] But the remedy to discover 'a new symbolic universe' as the reinstatement of the old is not feasible, and there is no hint how such treatment can be carried out. Another speaker at the same conference, the theologian Paul Tillich, provides the answer: 'the basic function of the conscience is to judge'.[38] Its voice must be trusted.

This judgement informs people what their true and their false self is. In that way their symbolic universe receives a firm basis so that they can withstand the danger of nihilism in spite of unfavourable social conditions. People who are not dedicated to 'a sensate, direct life of experience' can avoid the pitfalls of the protean self and those of the pseudo-religions. As their lives are meaningful, they are less likely to fall victim to mental illness, to drug addiction, or to suicidal or self-poisoning tendencies. They can thus meet the crisis in valuation. However, they cannot accept themselves as objects of social science, because in that position they would not be credited with personal freedom, and could only be the material for sociological analysis.

We must now investigate the part played in society's malaise by those who have been trained to treat the millions of mental patients, the drug addicts, those who are suicidal and the people who mutilate themselves. Such therapists claim professional status which means that they follow the principles of science to justify that claim. But those who are afflicted by the malaise are neither objects of a science of the mind nor objects of a science of society.

By deducing the patients' illnesses from a theory, the therapists reduce the psyche to some automatic functioning and the individual unique person to a manifestation of some impersonal force. The sciences of the mind are thus anti-spiritual. They can, however, serve a spiritual end by making patients aware of the factors which determine their mental health. In that way patients realize their personal freedom if they are *confronted* with the challenge they have to meet. Selfhood is the hallmark of the true person. How is that most precious endowment served by the various sciences of the mind?

2

SELFHOOD AND THE
SCIENCES OF THE MIND

———————————— • ————————————

In the field of mental health and mental illness, numerous theories and schools compete, each claiming scientific truth. The discussion will start with the most powerful school – organic psychiatry.

ORGANIC PSYCHIATRY

This school identifies the mind with the brain. Disturbances in the psyche are interpreted as cerebral disturbances. Neurological conditions present their victims with a challenge as they become aware of their failing mental powers, and from this awareness spiritual growth occurs. Senility, which is due to changes in the brain and affects thousands of old people, is by far the most common cerebro-mental disease. When advanced, patients are not aware of the challenge, but at the beginning of the illness, people recognize the failing of their memory and power of concentration. They have to face the fact that they cannot take responsibilities any more, they may have to retire and rely on others in a way they never had to before. Among other illnesses of the brain, multiple sclerosis presents a particularly difficult test for patients' acceptance of a fluctuating and often progressive mental impairment which can affect much younger age groups than senility. Symptoms include temporary blindness, slurred speech and, in the final stage of the illness, devastating mental deterioration. At that point, patients can no longer be expected to face and come to terms with their suffering.

The significance of such conditions as senility and multiple sclerosis for the cause of spiritual freedom consists in the refutation of the identity of mind and brain on the one hand, and in the acceptance of the limitations of spiritual freedom in cases of severe cerebral disturbance on the other.

If the mind were identical with the brain, sufferers from dementia and multiple sclerosis could not face their illness, as brain cells have no spiritual freedom. But during the final stages of these illnesses, this freedom is extinguished. It follows that psychotropic drugs, working on the brain, and electroconvulsions, applied to the brain, should be employed only in those cases in which patients are not in possession of spiritual freedom to cope with their emotional-mental problems. This insight is ignored by the claim made by William Sargant, one of the leaders of organic psychiatry: 'I feel safe in predicting that in the course of the next twenty-five years nearly all psychiatric patients will be readily cured with simple drugs mostly prescribed by general physicians'.[39]

This prediction is not likely to prove correct. Only in severe mental illness, in schizophrenia and in manic-depressive psychosis, have psychotropic drugs proved essential. Although such patients are objects of medical science, they maintain their freedom when they face their considerable suffering and agree to treatment (only a minority of such patients have to undergo treatment by coercion).

Followers of organic psychiatry are guilty of gross abuse: one author, a leading British psychiatrist, has come to the conclusion that 'in only one in about eight cases is a tranquillizer prescribed for some recognisable psychiatric disorder. All the rest seem to be given on account of ill-defined symptoms or in the hope of providing a solution to some personal problem'. The author voices his own response:

> It is questionable whether this prodigious prescription of tranquillizers is actually improving the quality of human existence. Indeed, it appears as if the situation foreseen by Aldous Huxley over forty years ago in his *Brave New World* has almost come to pass . . . if ever, by some unlucky chance, anything unpleasant should somehow happen, why, there's always Soma to give you a holiday from the facts. And there's always Soma to calm your anger, to reconcile you to your enemies, to make you patient and long-suffering. In the past you could only accomplish these things by making great effort and after years of hard moral training. Now you swallow two or three half-gram tablets and there you are. Anybody can be virtuous now. You can carry at least half your morality in a bottle. . . . Psychiatry without tears — that's what Soma is . . . the trouble is that it isn't.[40]

This criticism is not nearly strong enough. Many thousands of people have become addicted to tranquillizers. Their brains have been poisoned so that their minds have lost the freedom of spiritual wholeness, as they are unable to make decisions and take responsibility for their lives. Many have tried to break the drug habit, but that struggle for freedom is often out of their reach. They are aware of the challenge to regain their lost freedom and the awareness of that challenge represents a manifestation of their personal conscience which strives for a true self.

Even when the self has not been changed by the use of some form of psychiatric drug treatment, the mental illness itself may represent a challenge to integrate the unfamiliar disturbed self within the whole self. The patient's spirit may face the possibility of failure in this undertaking. Spiritual freedom would still be realized in making the supreme effort.[41]

THE PSYCHE–SOMA (MIND–BRAIN) CONUNDRUM

Donald M MacKay, while Granada Research Professor at the Department of Communication at the University of Keele in England, argued that spiritual freedom would be an illusion if every aspect of the psyche had its somatic equivalent, some cerebral mechanism, 'so that no change could take place in what we perceived, thought, believed etc, without some corresponding change taking place in the state of that [cerebral] mechanism'.[42]

As sufferers from senile dementia, multiple sclerosis and other cerebral illnesses lose their spiritual freedom in the terminal stages of their illness, does this mean that such freedom is just a manifestation of some cerebral mechanism? When answering this question, it is important to remember that spiritual freedom consists of making vital decisions which are involved in taking responsibility, in carrying out the demands of conscience.

In the case of those victims of cerebral illnesses where this capacity is lost, we are dealing with extreme cases of a cerebral-spiritual handicap. But MacKay 'exposed the folly of attempts to use brain science to deny human responsibility' in those who do not suffer from a cerebral disease, resulting in a loss of the capacity to make responsible decisions.

In order to prove the point, MacKay postulates that we are in a position to know the complete specification of a human brain, using some remote monitoring device. This specification would include the person's spiritual belief, his or her cognitive system and what he or she considers to be morally right and wrong. He calls his subject 'Joe'. He argues as follows:

> suppose we focus on the part or aspect of its [the brain's] mechanism that represents what Joe believes: Joe's *cognitive system*. We (presumably) can in principle frame a complete specification of this for ourselves; but if we ask whether Joe would be correct to believe our current specification, the answer must clearly be "No". [For] assuming that our specification is correct before Joe believes it, it cannot be so afterwards; for as soon as Joe believes it [,] his

brain must be in a new state different from the one it specifies. Nor would it help if we could invent a complete specification that would become correct *provided* that Joe believed it; for then *unless* Joe believed it [and he is free to reject such belief] it will be incorrect; so in spite of all our efforts, Joe would not be in error if he disbelieved it. In short, no *complete specification* of Joe's cognitive system exists that has an unconditional, take-it-or-leave-it claim on Joe's assent.

The reason for the preservation of Joe's freedom to decide what he believes lies in the fact that by exercising his freedom to believe, the state of his brain alters, and the previous state no longer exists.[43] Thus, personal freedom and responsibility, the attributes of spiritual holism, are saved from being considered delusional.

The science of neurophysiology, the knowledge of cerebral states, is not relevant for the state of ethical freedom. It was Erwin W Straus's aim to decipher the unwritten constitution of everyday life; he practised neurology and psychiatry in Germany and was appointed Professor of Psychology in America. He pointed out that such knowledge is not concerned with brain material, but with conceptual products of scientific knowledge, such as cellular structures which include neural synapses:

> The brain explored by the neurophysiologist and the brain with which the mind enters into liaison are not the same . . . When [the scientist] invites the mind to enter into liaison with the brain, the brain undergoes a sudden metamorphosis . . . We cannot ignore [the fact] that two brains are involved in neurophysiological research: the brain observed and the observer's brain . . . The observer, not the observed, is responsible for an observation . . . it is the observer who describes and reports [on] an experiment . . . the observer's brain does not know of any other brain [has, in fact, no knowledge at all].

According to another author, 'the concepts that we gather under the term "mental" are only names given to various aspects of the functions of the cerebral cortex'. Straus asks:

> If the information given by the author is nothing but an echo of events in his own cortex, are we not forced to conclude that the individual cortex must actually know itself? If this were so, we should wonder that – instead of mere intuition – the full exertion of neurophysiological research is required and how it is possible. Furthermore, how can we account for the fact that the knowledgeable cortex needs, in spite of its own microstructure, instruments of magnification in the exploration of other brains?[44]

With these remarks, Straus refutes the alleged neurophysiological basis of the mind. Brains never construct, only minds do, and, as Straus points out, the scientific object, whether the scientist is aware of the truth or not, is a mental construct. There are thus not the separate realms of extended bodies and knowing minds, as Descartes taught. In fact, the bodies are, in Kant's language, appearances in the outer sense; they can be correlated with the appearances of the inner sense, which means that mental attributes such as seeing, feeling and knowing can be located in parts of the brain, but there is no interaction of a mental and a physical activity. In Kant's words:

> the much-discussed question of the communion between the thinking and the extended . . . comes then simply to this: *how in a thinking subject outer intuition*, namely that of space, with its filling-in of figure and motion, *is possible*. And this is a question which no human being can possibly answer. This gap in our knowledge can never be filled.[45]

The mind-body or psyche-soma conundrum cannot be solved. The formulation of Gabriel Marcel, a French philosopher concerned with existence, should be accepted. According to his view, the union of the body with the soul is not a problem, it is a mystery.[46] The recognition and appreciation of this mystery is the ultimate gain for the acceptance of spiritual freedom by organic psychiatry, which is concerned with the cerebral disturbances of the whole person.

BEHAVIOUR THERAPY

Scientists cannot accept mysteries which include those of the person, the subject. Thus, behaviour scientists eliminate the patients' minds and focus on their bodily behaviour, the object. They themselves refute this dogma if they demand from their therapists that they show warmth, concern and responsiveness to their patients' needs.[47]

While this non-scientific personal behaviour of therapists in meeting the non-scientific needs of the patients has been admitted, it is maintained that therapists hand patients a tool which consists of a scientific technique. Neurotic behaviour is said to be the result of faulty learning, to be corrected by the appropriate stimuli.

This conception of people can be refuted. Pavlov's miserable hungry dogs, encased in a frame, isolated from their normal surroundings, with holes in their necks to collect saliva, did salivate at the sound of a bell which had previously been sounded each time that juicy meat was offered. But under normal circumstances dogs, other animals and people do not behave in that way, in response to isolated stimuli, unconditioned or conditioned. Normal behaviour in animals is purposive seeking food or a mate, while human beings look for a purposeful, creative life. Beneficial results must not be interpreted in terms of this faulty theory which is an insult to human beings.

Aversion techniques   Painful stimuli such as electric shocks are applied for instance to an alcoholic when he or she is offered a favourite drink. This treatment does not rely on breaking an association between drink and pleasure, but relies for its success on the patient's response, not to the painful current, but from his or her conscience which asks the patient to give up alcohol. The treatment fails if the adaptive responses 'are not already in the patient's repertoire of behaviour'.[48] We are not surprised that 'there is little empirical evidence' that the painful stimulus establishes a conditioned anxiety response in the alcoholic.

Modelling   The therapist demonstrates to a patient behaviour which is appropriate in certain circumstances. This 'technique' has been adopted by countless parents in bringing up their children, its success depending not on the automatic reflex response to a 'stimulus', but on the child's experience of parental love, a supreme manifestation of spiritual whole- ness. The shy and insecure adult who models himself or herself on the therapist's behaviour can only be helped if the spiritual qualities of mutual trust and respect are applied.

Operant conditioning   This technique hides spirituality behind a pseudo- scientific cloak. It encourages 'good', which means healthy behaviour, by offering rewards and by refusing them in the case of 'bad', unhealthy behaviour. There is, of course, no automatic stimulus–response in such measures. As with 'modelling', the results depend, as all parents know, on co-operation: children and adults accept encouragement and discourage- ment freely as aids in their development.

Desensitization   This term is correctly used to overcome allergies by injecting patients with small amounts of a substance to which they are sensitive and making them insensitive. The technique is applied behav- iourally to help people suffering from phobias – for instance, an irrational fear of cats. Patients are exposed to the sight of the feared object first at a distance, then later at close range. The success entirely depends on the person finding the courage to bear the anxiety, which is related to the dreaded 'stimulus'. Courage is, of course, the hallmark of spiritual con- duct, and conduct is judged to be correct if people take responsibility for their deeds, thus accepting their obligations. The theory of behaviour therapy however is not founded on such a principle, because it reduces people to robots – in other words, denigrated human beings. But the applications of this theory provide patients with opportunities to prove their spirituality.

THE COGNITIVE APPROACH

Behaviour therapists have recently added an important approach to that of modifying behaviour by using the techniques of aversion, modelling, operant conditioning and desentization. They *confront* patients with the way in which their disturbed minds are working, so that those who suffer from depression, anxiety, obsessions and lack of confidence can recognize why they are ill and how they can liberate themselves from their illness. Although the authors of the method of modifying behaviour in this way claim that they are simply using 'techniques' to enable patients to alter their behaviour, the therapists appeal, in fact, to people's spiritual freedom, as their approach is to ask people to reflect on the way in which their minds work and to face their disturbed emotional life. Not only are the sufferers made aware of the way they feel and think, they are even expected to estimate the strength of their anxieties and depressions, and their failure to cope with their lives, by noting the degree of their failures and successes, giving themselves marks, say, from 0 to 10.

Those who are frightened to go shopping or swimming, for example, provided that they are determined to be free from their fears, are encouraged to attain full freedom from their handicap by making very gradual efforts to master the feared situation, encouraged by the therapist who often accompanies the sufferers on their outings.

Patients are also made aware of the important fact that their feelings of anxiety become less and less severe as they persevere with their treatment. This in turn gives them the valour to continue with their efforts.

People learn that running away from feared situations and avoiding decisions do not solve their problems. They realize that their conscience expects them to get on with life, even if that means tolerating their fears. Any success in overcoming their phobias provides encouragement.

It may well be a great relief if a patient, plagued by obsessive thoughts, responds to the suggestion that the thought should be exaggerated and then discovers that the exaggeration is still bearable. Again, the therapist expects people with this type of problem to find the courage to bear their suffering so that they can credit themselves with a moral victory, gaining encouragement and self-confidence.

If people learn to avoid linking a cup of coffee after their meal with a cigarette, this success is not one which amounts to 'stimulus control', but one that has gained control over their smoking habit: neither the tasting of the coffee nor the relief that inhaling cigarette smoke gives are stimuli which automatically have responses. The operative factor is the element of freedom gained by the decision to relinquish the smoking habit.

Those who overcome food addictions that lead to obesity are not helped, as certain authors claim, by:

> modifications of the food stimulus which would have led to the response of overeating, but are helped by their free decision to accept a programme, proposed by their therapists which consists in recording every food consumed in a diary, thus being well aware of the quantity they eat, furthermore in noting time, place and circumstances as well as the mood before and after eating.[One woman learnt from this that] sadness and boredom were likely to result in 'binge' eating. This knowledge was helpful as such moods could be borne without 'bingeing'. Further clues were important: biscuits and sweets represented the biggest problem and could be avoided. This woman agreed to sit down in the dining room when having regular meals, to concentrate on the process of eating, its enjoyment and to leave some food on her plate. She was not asked to starve herself. She lost over five stones, maintained her weight, joined squash and tennis clubs with the result of gaining better health and a great deal of satisfaction.

A man who had served a prison sentence for indecent exposure to young women was able to liberate himself from his abnormal sexual urge by being encouraged to imagine situations which would act as an antidote to his sexual arousal. One fantasy was of a woman ridiculing his sexual exhibition, another of being assaulted by the woman's boyfriend. Describing the 'aversive' scene changed the patient from being sexually excited to being tremulous and anxious. Thus, his perverted sexual arousal dropped considerably when measured on a scale from 0 to 8. The fantasies were repeated at least six times in every session, with the result that the man could walk in the park without his usual problem of sexual urge and fear. The next step was for him to learn more about sex and masturbation. After three months, the man was able to start a normal relationship with a girl.

Cognitive therapists help patients to change their attitudes which cause them suffering and therefore enable them to realize their true selves. Such treatment should, however, not be conceived in mechanistic, scientific and technical terms.[49]

Our next task is to examine psychoanalysis from the true-self point of view.

PSYCHOANALYSIS

Freud presented the human spirit with a fundamental challenge. His work raises doubts regarding the attainment of self-knowledge, an essential premise of the true-self ethic. As pointed out by David Dewhurst, a lecturer in the philosophy of education at the University of Tasmania:

> feelings merge, and are submerged. The reason that someone may not recognize his feelings of guilt may be that other feelings, such as anger, have predominated rather as the tide can do over a flowing stream . . . [the person] fails to notice that he *does* feel guilt, and thereby fails to appreciate an important fact about himself. Especially, motives and purposes are in doubt. 'Is it self-love or pure duty that has impelled me?' asks the searcher for true knowledge. He may be forced to admit that somebody else may know him better than he knows himself, as he may have blind-spots which do not let him see his true nature. Thus, self-knowledge should perhaps be built on what others convey as their knowledge of a person. There is the possibility that the understanding of oneself may be enhanced by the perceptive comments of others; by their observations that one looks anxious or hurt or pleased or sad for instance, that one is acting defensively or aggressively and so on. . . . It may also be that part of the process of self-knowledge involves the willingness to draw the sorts of inferences from one's own behaviour that one draws from the behaviour of others.[50]

By stressing the importance of the unconscious, Freud has enriched people's spiritual lives, as they are aware of the need to take into consideration the possibility of self-deceit. Each person's conscience will demand that he or she should discover and face his or her hidden true self. Freud's emphasis on the unconscious, powerful instinctual forces of the mind has important spiritual significance, as people realize that they must face and deal with the instinctual side of their nature.

But Freud's own interpretation sabotages the exercise of such freedom: the instinctual forces determine people's emotional lives; they are turned into libidinal beings and those who are close to them, such as their parents, become libidinal objects. In a truly scientific spirit, human beings lose the uniqueness of their individuality.

As a result of such scientific treatment, love, the supreme spiritual human achievement, is defined by Freud as follows:

> the nucleus of what we mean by love naturally consists (and this is what is commonly called love, and what the poets sing of) in sexual love with sexual union as its aim. But we do not separate from this – what in any case has a share in the name 'love' – on the one hand, self-love, and on the other love for parents and children, friendship and love for humanity in general, and also devotion to concrete objects and to abstract ideas. . . . Our justification lies in the fact that psycho-analytic research has taught us that all these tendencies are an expression of the same instinctive activities.[51]

This 'justification' is only valid because according to Freud all human activities are libidinal, therefore love must be libidinal.

According to Heinz Kohurt, one of Freud's followers, the libido plays:

> not only a significant role in mature object relationships . . . but it is also the main source of libidinal fuel for some of the socio-cultural important activities which are subsumed under the term creativity, and it forms a component of that highly esteemed human attitude to which we refer as wisdom.[52]

The mechanism by which sexual energy is transformed into non-sexual activity is called 'sublimation'. But as Michael Polanyi, a member of the American Academy of Arts and Sciences and of the International Academy of the Philosophy of Science, has pointed out, 'sublimation is a circumlocution which relies for its meaning entirely on our previous understanding of the things which it is supposed to explain'.[53]

Viktor E Frankl, who survived confinement in a Nazi concentration camp, as professor of Psychiatry at the University of Vienna formulated a form of psychotherapy which considers spiritual values to be of crucial importance. He has stressed the spiritual objection to the interpretation of human relations in terms of instinctual energy: relationships between people are an expression of personal freedom which involves taking responsibility for another person. But the biological sexual instinct is automatic in character, its responses being directed at members of society in general.[54]

As according to Freud behaviour is basically instinctual and as instincts seek pleasurable gratification, the gaining of pleasure is said to express man's ultimate aim. While allowance is made for facing unpleasant reality, the striving for pleasure would only be delayed. Freud speaks as a psychologist and thus his hedonism is psychological, but it leads to ethical hedonism, to the view that man *ought* to make pleasure his ultimate aim.

Both forms of the pleasure principle are false, as people engage in many activities which are not pleasurable, whether we think of a mother looking after her sick child or of a soldier enduring hardship in front of enemy fire. These people are motivated by what their conscience demands of them and act according to its ethic.

This account does not mean that life cannot be full of pleasure. But pleasure eludes those who strive for it. It occurs spontaneously when we encounter a sight that strikes us as beautiful or when we hear the lovely song of a bird or the sound of an orchestra. We also gain pleasure from having acted according to some moral demand; we are pleased that we had the required strength.

If we make pleasure our aim, we end up with disillusionment, with pain. We have seen that von Bertalanffy listed psychoanalysis amongst the pseudo-religions, together with soap operas which express television pleasure seeking, and we have encountered another facet of the pleasure principle in Sennet's description of the protean self, 'a creature of immediate appearance and sensations', in danger of drug addiction and of an empty existence.

Freud's own conceptual world is devoid of pleasure. The unconscious is dominated by the hapless Oedipus. He was never guilty of immoral intention but was made guilty as the plaything of a Greek god, made to kill his father and marry his mother. Freud's patients are made to suffer the Oedipus complex; they have to bear an ambivalent relationship to one parent and murderous hostility to the other parent.

There is serious trouble from the strict authoritarian super-ego which represents the inhibitions of man's alleged basic instincts. The super-ego is Freud's concept of conscience. It extorts obedience from the child by threatening the unbearable loss of parental love. This interpretation of the moral agency is utterly different from the interpretation by the ethic of conscience. This ethic relies on a person's own judgement, on ethical-spiritual freedom and not on outside coercion. A further objection to Freudian concept is that it involves the theory in linguistic error.

David Jones, an American doctor of philosophy, has pointed out that Freud's explanation of the genesis and function of moral conscience in human beings is false, as this interpretation of conscience means that the more moral a person is, the more he suffers from his conscience. In fact,

> the moral feelings of shame, guilt and remorse, are appropriate only when a person has [done] what he *consciously believes* is unworthy, wrong, immoral, not when he unconsciously complied with unconscious threats . . . Freud was not talking about a bad conscience in the moral sense, but about an efficient, 'good' conscience in the psycho-analytic sense.[55]

Guilt is not guilt, but anxiety, produced by the punitive superego. It follows that the aim of the treatment is to make a person less moral, less subject to his superego, to his conscience, which means being less anxiety-ridden and less inhibited. In fact,

> the history of the person's *repression* of dangerous id-impulses (instincts), however important it may be in explaining his present personality, does not account for that part of the person's psychology which enables him to think, feel and act as a morally sincere person.[56]

Thus, patients, lying on the couches of psychoanalysts are being brainwashed: they are made to believe that their anxieties are the result of a repression of their instincts by their conscience and that they can obtain relief by instinctual awareness.

Apart from sexuality, Freud postulated aggressiveness as a primary instinct. The cultural superego is said to have held in check an aggression which threatens to destroy civilization. It succeeds by threatening to punish the libidinal aggression by an 'anxiety of conscience' – in other words, it represses instinctive behaviour by fear of punishment.

The true-self ethic does not concur with Freud's idea that there is a 'primary hostility of men towards one another' which has to be kept under control by a cultural conscience. The true-self ethic does not battle with conscience to 'moderate its demands'.[57] Instead, it relies on the communal feelings of tolerance, sympathy and love among people. Where aggressiveness takes over, the ethic relies on the power of true conscience to enable people to transcend their aggressive tendencies.

Not all Freudians have accepted the biological instinctual interpretation of the libido. One psychoanalyst, W R O Fairbairn, for instance, developed an alternative theory, according to which a person's development and fulfilment or frustration depend on their relationship with objects. The object is considered the 'ultimate goal' of the libido. True-self therapists can agree with Fairbairn that 'it is essential that a child should be helped to develop a self-confident and strong individuality of his own, as a person in his own right capable of entering into relationships with other persons without danger to his own integrity as a person'.[58] True-self therapists can further agree that the baby depends on a mature and satisfying mother, but they cannot agree that this development is in terms of libidinal energy which was scientifically conceived. Nor can they accept the patient's need to transfer his or her feelings of love and hate to the therapist after having regressed to babyhood when the emotional disturbance was said to have occurred. True-self therapists are encouraged in this view by H H Strupp, an American investigator, who found that 'psychotherapeutic change does not depend on the elucidation of historical antecedents but on the reliving and modification of historically meaningful patterns that come alive in the patient-therapist relationship'. He holds that reinstitution and resolution of a quasi-parent-child relationship represents only one approach, but he sees no reason to suppose that it is the only or best approach. What is crucial is the quality of the interpersonal experience between the patient and the therapist.[59]

As far as the therapist is concerned, another writer, Kevin Mitchell, has confirmed the validity of spiritual holism.[60] He believes that the following qualities are required:

1   *Accurate empathy* Therapists must be sensitive to the current feelings and thoughts of their patients and must be able to communicate their understanding of their patients' feelings and thinking, and must use a language which is attuned to their patients.

2 *Non-possessive warmth* The extent to which the therapist communicates a non-judgemental, caring and positive regard for the patient as a person, although not necessarily condoning the patient's behaviour.

3 *Genuineness* The extent to which the therapist is not defensive or phoney in his interaction with his patients.

Freud did not tolerate any deviation from the teachings of the school he had founded, but, like the representatives of the other schools of depth psychology, he insisted that therapists should undergo a thorough training analysis. This was considered necessary so that analysts could learn the technique, remove their repressions in order to recognize them in their patients and, finally, be prevented from expressing their unresolved love/hate tendencies in the treatment. But research concerned with the training of psychotherapists revealed that the results of the treatment did not depend on the school to which therapists belonged nor whether they had received a personal analysis. A successful interaction of the personalities of patient and therapist was not found to be affected by these two factors.[61]

While Freud and his followers carried out the investigation into the mental world in the same scientific spirit as his teachers had investigated the physical world,[62] the true-self therapist prefers a non-scientific ethical – spiritual approach. The contrast between the two approaches is demonstrated by the following comments on a dream interpretation, carried out by a follower of Melanie Klein, who was a pioneer in the object relationship theory.

KLEINIAN PSYCHOANALYSIS

A Kleinian Dream Interpretation

A man reported to his woman analyst: 'I had a dream last night in which my head was being squashed by someone sitting on my face.' The therapist assumed that this dream reflected the patient's regression to the time when he was a baby and was experiencing the vital relationship with his mother's breast. He was regarded as still at the breast. But in the dream, where there should have been a mouth–breast relationship, a face was pressed against the buttocks. The therapist was able to argue to herself that this must be derived from a distortion of the assumed feeding relationship. She therefore offered the following interpretation: 'Because of your envy, you are unable to take the good milk of my interpretations. Instead you take in my words as poisonous faeces.'

The critic who reported this case, suggested that the squashing of the patient's head may have meant that he was unable to think as a result of his therapist's dogmatic interpretations. The notion of poisonous faeces did not come 'out of the patient's own thinking but from the therapist's theoretical orientation'.

The patient's response to this interpretation was to remain silent, and then to appear to change the subject. He eventually came out of this silence with the following statement: 'I am going to the USA for my holiday, but I don't speak English [the analysis occurred in Latin America]. This will make me very vulnerable because it means that I will have to be totally dependent on my wife to explain to me everything that is being said.' Again, the therapist interpreted the patient's concern in terms of the anxiety which babies feel when they are separated from their parents.[63]

But this man was not a helpless baby. It was harmful to regress him to his early childhood as he required the freedom of his adulthood to cope with the adventure of his life's journey. The dependency on his wife was utterly different from the baby's dependency on a mother and he needed encouragement so that he could cope with the planned situation. This patient was right to object to the suffocating treatment, to the libidinal interpretation of sucking his mother's milk or some other instinctual gratification. Psychoanalysis fails because invariably it explains adulthood in terms of the unconscious dynamics of babyhood. It applies the same principle to the analysis of children, but here, as elsewhere in its field, there is disagreement regarding factual truth. Thus, Otto Fenichel contradicts Melanie Klein when he says that an 'exaggerated desire to destroy appears in some children, but is not active in every infant sucking at the mother's breast'.[64]

JUNG'S ANALYTICAL PSYCHOLOGY

Psychoanalysis confines its attention to the personal unconscious, which is formed from repressed infantile impulses, wishes, sublimal perceptions and forgotten experiences. C G Jung added as an object of study the collective unconscious, a deeper stratum which gives rise to the archetypes, 'primordial images [which] appear in dreams, unusual states of mind, or psychotic fantasies'.[65] These archetypes affect human behaviour and thought, and have been named the persona, the anima and animus, the old wise man, the earth mother, the shadow and the self.[66]

Such fundamental experiences are accepted by the holistic spiritual point of view as challenges which the individual person's conscience has to meet in its freedom. But this is not Jung's interpretation. He stated in his autobiography that: 'My life is a story of the self-realization of the unconscious. Everything in the unconscious seeks outward manifestation'.[67] Hence it is a story without freedom, without responsibility.

Jung has illustrated the way in which the anima, the female archetype, exercises its power: 'When, for instance, a highly honoured scholar in his seventies deserts his family and marries a 20-year-old red-haired actress, then we know that the gods have claimed another victim. It is thus that demonic supremacy shows itself to us.'[68] But those who strive to achieve their true self by taking responsibility for their lives object to such fatalism. They consider the 'highly honoured scholar' to have been free to resist his infatuation, as Goethe did when in his old age he fell in love with a 16-year-old girl. They are saved from the Jungian indoctrination, according to which the anima has 'a superior knowledge of the laws of life' and they do not believe that 'behind all the anima's cruel sporting with human fate there lies something like a secret intention'. Their lives are not made meaningful by the expectation that 'the anima loses its impetuous, impulsive and compulsive character'.[69] They consider it their duty to overcome their own destructive tendencies such as hatred and irritability. Not having been initiated into Jungian mythology, they cannot escape from personal responsibility by blaming their 'dark side' on the shadow archetype which 'is all those uncivilised desires and emotions that are incompatible with social standards and our ideal personality, all that we are ashamed of'. The non-initiated do not agree that 'trying to live as better and nobler people . . . involves us in endless hypocrisy and deceit', nor do they agree that it 'imposes such a strain on us that we often collapse and become worse than we need have been'.[70]

Underlying the postulate of the personal and the collective unconscious with its archetypal manifestations is a scientific basis, as Jung conceived the libido as a 'psychic energy' to be 'the foundation and regulator of all psychic existence'.[71]

THE CLINICAL EVALUATION OF DYNAMIC PSYCHOTHERAPY

Freudians, Kleinians, Jungians and others claim that they benefit the forces that operate in the human psyche. These claims have been evaluated by psychiatrists who use control assessments and compare a large number of patients who have been treated with such dynamic methods with the same number of patients who are equally ill but who received no treatments – for instance, some patients were put on a waiting list and assessed clinically after a certain time, while others received psychotherapy during the same period.

The following criteria for success were demanded: doctors and patients should record that symptoms of emotional distress had lessened, people's ability to work had improved and people were less liable to break down, which meant that they were less vulnerable.

A recent report by Gavin Andrews which reviews a large number of such assessments has come to the conclusion that there is no evidence that dynamic psychotherapies are, in fact, successful. Improvements in patients occur spontaneously in the course of time.

Andrews affirms that those who practise dynamic psychotherapies not only fail to help patients, but they may even harm them. In particular, he mentions unacceptable sexual relationships with patients; these have been reported by a number of writers. Furthermore, 10 per cent of mental health professionals who underwent the obligatory training analysis considered that the experience had been harmful. Therefore 'the number of patients harmed who do not complain might be considerable'. The conclusion is that the treatment which is not beneficial and may even be harmful should be discontinued, especially as it is costly in time and money for therapists and patients alike.

The argument is flawed: a clinical evaluation cannot do justice to a personal involvement, especially of the intensity which occurs in dynamic psychotherapy. Patients who have received such treatment cannot be compared with those who have had no personal treatment. Dependency on the therapist is subject to criticism as the strong feelings of love and hate which the patient felt for his or her parents can be transferred to the therapist. Whether symptoms of emotional suffering improve or whether patients can cope better with their lives after treatment, the relationship with their therapist is of great importance to them, although in certain cases the relationship may have been harmful.

The writer of the article prefaces his rejection of dynamic psychotherapies with the statement that Freud had 'contributed considerably to our understanding of human life, and his ideas have humanised society', but that 'the importance of his ideas does not mean that treatments, derived from his work, are automatically valid'.[72]

One would expect that the 'considerable understanding' of human life in general would benefit those who are treated on the same sound principles if they suffer from emotional disturbances, especially as Freud's views on the 'normal' psyche were derived from his interpretations of the disturbed psyche. The enormous contribution which Freud and his followers have made to our understanding of human life consists of making people aware, which means making them conscious of their instinctual urges and, in the case of Jung, of the role of the 'archetypal forces' of which we were unaware – that is, the unconscious.

But that awareness has to be qualified. Followers of dynamic psychotherapies wrongly claim that their libidinal approach is scientific and has enabled them to discover contents in the unconscious which are observable by patients and therapists which then should lead to beneficial changes. For instance, the patient who has been made aware of her hatred of her mother should overcome her hatred. But, as a contemporary philosopher–psychiatrist has pointed out, this is a fundamental mistake. The insight does not help and the analysis continues year after year. What is required is *reflection*,[73] true-self ethic reflection – that is, how do I cope with the instinctual or archetypal aspects of my personality? Thus, people who are mentally free can meet a challenge without being objects of a science of the mind. As dynamic psychotherapists omit the vital change to true-self ethic, the critic is correct when he stresses the unfortunate 'influence on patients' ethical and moral values'.[74]

GESTALT ENCOUNTER

Scientific psychodynamic accounts of the psyche tend to sabotage the practice of the true-self ethic and thus to confuse spiritual holistic striving by their denial of personal freedom. The school of a Gestalt conception leads to an encounter treatment which adds to the damage from the scientific approach.

The German term 'Gestalt' stands for configuration, which is said to consist of two spatial entities, the organism and its environment. At the boundary between the two the (non-spatial) self is situated. It contacts the environment and belongs to both the environment and the organism.[75] This holistic structure in no way conforms to a holistic spiritual view. It is described partly in biological and partly in psychological terms and is said to manifest itself by denigrating the principles of the true-self ethic: thus, organic growth is identified in non-biological terms, and organisms are said to be afraid to take initiatives and responsibility.[76]

It is claimed that 'annihilating, destroying, initiative, and anger are essential to growth in the organism/environmental field . . . they are always "healthy" . . . they are irreducible without loss of valuable parts of the personality, especially self-confidence, feeling and creativity'. The confusion of biological and psychological functions is heightened by the statement that 'destroying is a function of appetite'. This is illustrated as follows:

> every organism in a field grows by incorporating, digesting, and assimilating new matter, and this requires destroying the existing form to its assimilable elements, whether it be food, a lecture, a father's influence, the difference between a mate's domestic habits and one's own.

A moral application of this hybrid conception is expressed thus:

> the warm pleasurable (and angry) destroying of existing forms in personal relations often leads to mutual advantage and love, as in the seduction and defloration of a shy virgin, or in the breaking down of prejudices between friends.

People are told,

> Do not be afraid that by dissolving conscience you will become a criminal or an impulsive psychopath. You will be surprised when you allow organic self-regulation to develop and your outgoing drives to contact other persons, how the principles that *you* ought to live by will seem to emerge from your very bones and will be *obviously appropriate* for living out regardless of the social situation you are in.[77]

It is not surprising that in the encounter group, meeting under the leadership of a Gestalt therapist, his message caused casualties. In one study 'ten per cent of the people attending a set of 17 encounter groups became casualties'. A casualty is defined as one who suffered considerable and persistent psychological distress as a result of his encounter group experience.[78] Even those who do not show signs of distress suffer from a distortion of their self-image.

ADLER'S INDIVIDUAL PSYCHOLOGY

Neurological, reflexological, libidinal and biological mechanisms cannot account for the spiritual freedom and personal responsibility which is demanded by the true-self ethic. Adler claimed that he had created a science of individual psychology which is not based on the study of mechanisms but which is teleological – that is, it is concerned with the study of aims or goals. These, he claimed, were manifest in everyone's lifestyle. As people are embedded in a social milieu, Adler defined a healthy and necessary human purpose as one which serves society, a purpose expressed in social interest. This orientation brought him into conflict with Freud, especially with the acceptance of aggressiveness as a primary instinct, and led to a demand for a mental hygiene which is based on the ethical rights of the community. What society had Adler in mind? Not the present one which has lost its bearings, suffers from a crisis in valuation, and which has given rise to the protean self which has no core of innateness. His insight into psychopathology can be applied thus: many patients feel inferior as they believe they have lost out in the competitive struggle. But his interpretation is not valid; people will not be educated to accept the interests of society, if their striving for power reveals them to be spoiled and pampered. Alcoholics and drug addicts did not start their habit with a superiority complex, longing for power.[79] It is true that in many cases addicts try (in vain) to alleviate unbearable situations. The society in which they live has failed to offer acceptable conditions.

Adler's dream interpretations similarly are not valid. He interprets dreams in terms of their social interest – for example, in a dream, it is stated that:

> the individual's goal of achievement remains the same as in waking life, but a dream impels him toward that goal with increased emotional power . . . In dreams we produce the pictures which will arouse the feelings and emotions which we need for our purposes, that is, for solving the problems confronting us at the time of the dream, in accordance with the particular style of life which is ours.

Thus, a dream of falling is said to point to a fear of losing prestige and a dream that involves dead people means that 'the dreamer has not yet finally buried his dead and remains under the dead person's influence' – that is, he is not playing his full part in society. Dreams of missing a train or an opportunity 'can be shown in most cases to be the expression of an established character trait, namely, escaping from a dreaded defeat by arriving too late or by letting an opportunity slip'.[80]

Some problems are not the result of people's social ambitions or social maturity. For example, a dream of falling may indicate that a person has lost a foothold in life and thus his or her confidence; a dream of dead people may be a reminder of the influence his or her dead father had upon the person. However, the dream does not mean that the influence should be 'buried' or abolished. Dreams of missing trains or missed opportunities may not indicate a tendency to escape from life, rather a challenge to cope with it.

Adler's interpretation of children's bedwetting dreams is false and cruel. He says that 'children who wet their beds often dream that they are urinating at the proper place. In this rather cowardly fashion they find it easy to express their grievance and revenge at the feeling of being neglected [by their parents who stand for society]'.[81] In fact, society's disapproval hangs over the child as a terrible scourge. Bedwetting is an involuntary act and is not motivated by any cowardly feeling of revenge against society.

Not only in dream interpretations does the Adlerian system fail. Applying his ideas to behaviour, people are 'persuaded' to accept a point of view without being given a choice. Their lifestyle is forced into the straitjacket of the 'social interest'. The following can serve as an illustration of such an imposition.

On the mornings of schooldays, an 11-year-old girl is 'so nervous that the whole house suffers'. Although the child is obviously terrified of school, her feelings are not acknowledged by the social scientist who insists that

> she enjoys complete domination over her family [by expressing her terror], yet does not understand this fact in its context [of the Adlerian theory]. [Thus] if she could be made to realize the truth [of the theory], if we could show her that the extreme overrating of the everyday problems of school is nothing but bragging and constructing an alibi for possible failure to excel at school, we should be taking an important step in the right direction. We may have to go further, and show her what type of person brags.

Now follow two revelations, the first being very discouraging for the unfortunate child: 'No one will try to impress other people unless he believes that his actual accomplishments give insufficient testimony of his personal importance'. But surely the child must rate her accomplishments at school to provide sufficient testimony of her personal importance? The second revelation fails to consider the child's vulnerability: 'it is evident that [such a person] is too much dependent on the opinion of others'. Thus, to the already present terror of school that the girl suffered was added the feeling of guilt towards her family and shame on account of poor performance in her lessons. A dose of irony is added: 'If my opinion is correct, you are quite right in acting as you do – perhaps you should even do more. Everything you do goes to prove that you are a very bright girl who has found the right way of impressing her environment.' Adler is confident that he has successfully applied his social science. After what to him is the child's 'demonstration before her family', she is supposed to:

> think to herself: 'Dr Adler would say that I did that just to show off' . . . And the time will come when, in the very midst of the tumult, she will remember how her conduct would appear to me, and this self-consciousness alone will effect a great improvement. And finally she will wake up in the morning with the realization: 'Now I'm about to stir up a commotion in the family'. And being aware of it, she can then avoid it.[82]

Such a success is a failure from the point of view of the true-self ethic, as the patient was not allowed to discover the correct reason for her school phobia. She was denied her personal freedom. Adler's normative social science fails to meet the ethical needs of his patients. Only an ethic which is based on the acceptance of personal responsibility in general (which includes the social domain) could create a society which is free of the many iniquities that cause current mental suffering.

The scientific frameworks of neurological, reflexological, libidinal and archetypal mechanisms, and of teleological social interest are obstacles to the realization of a holistic spiritual ethic of the true self. Further obstacles to the achievement of this vital aim exist, and we must face these obstacles and make an effort to overcome them. The problem is how to reconcile the ethical freedom of people's spirituality with their factual social en-meshment, with their bodily constitution, which is imposed on them and which may result in incapacitating illness, and finally, with their mortality. We cannot explain people's dual nature – their ethical freedom and their imposed necessity (determinism). For by explaining any situation, we subsume a particular matter as under a principle that covers the phenome-non that we want to explain. For instance, a doctor explains a patient's breathlessness as the result of a cardiac weakness which interferes with the normal actions of the lungs. Thus, a subjective symptom is explained by reference to an objective bodily state which covers the situation. But if we can *describe* the dual nature of the human person, we can clarify what is involved in our humanity, and thus illuminate our spiritual and biological wholeness without dissecting it, allowing the principle of wholeness to be respected.

Such a description, however, of our human situation does not amount to an understanding of our ethical freedom. We cannot grasp a person's dual nature.[83] We may simply call it incomprehensible or 'mysterious', as the missionary doctor and gifted organist Albert Schweitzer did.[84] We shall start with a description of the way in which the unique person and his or her ethical freedom is endangered by a crowd of fellow human beings who present a challenge to that person's spirituality.

3

SPIRITUAL CHALLENGES

———————————— • ————————————

THE THREAT OF ANONYMITY

People who accept the sciences of the mind are reduced to instances of a general system of thought. They lose their uniqueness and cannot be credited with personal moral freedom because of the deterministic character of science. We saw in chapter 1 that certain writers who are concerned with the human social structure, its functions and its changes have illuminated the tragic loss of uniqueness which so many have suffered in the Western world. Karl Mannheim's diagnosis of the crisis in valuation and von Bertalanffy's demonstration of the damaging effects of the loss of the symbolic universe added to our understanding of why people feel nameless, anonymous.

Richard Sennett added a further dimension to the escape from genuineness: the replacement of the authentic self by the 'protean self' which is 'a creature of immediate appearances and sensations, "direct" experiences with people', seeking constantly self-revelations which fail to be gained (*see* pages 19–20).

In his illumination of the essence of a person's being, Martin Heidegger has emphasized the constant threat to the authentic person from the anonymous crowd. One of Heidegger's commentators has reminded us that:

> each man is sheerly uninterchangeable, no one can stand in for him there, no one can take his being off him and bear it for him. But in everyday being-together, man turns away from the possibility which is most his own and understands himself from his worldish possibilities among other selves. In his everydayness, man in advance measures his own self by what the others are and have, by what they have achieved and failed to achieve in the world. . . . In everyday being-together man is not himself, the others have taken his being off him. But who are the others? They are not this one or that one, not anybody or the sum of all: 'they' are just 'people', the people of whom we

may say 'people think so', and 'people don't wear that any more' . . . 'they', the others, are not any definite others, they are essentially interchangeable; anyone can stand in for everybody else, anybody can represent and substitute anyone else . . . It is *not* man himself who is *there*, but it is 'they', people who are there . . . the everyday self is the they.[85]

Communication turns into gossiping and passing the word along. Things are so because people say so. The result is idle talk which spreads from vocal gossip to writing, scribbling and feeding on superficial reading. According to Heidegger, 'Idle talk is the possibility of understanding everything without previously making the thing one's own . . . Idle talk controls even the ways in which one may be curious. It says what one "must" have read and seen'. People cannot be true to themselves or others as members of the 'they', the anonymous crowd where clarity is replaced by ambiguity. 'In the ambiguity of the way things have been publicly interpreted, talking about things ahead of the game and making surmises about them curiously, gets passed off as what is really happening, while taking action and carrying something through gets stamped as something merely subsequent and unimportant . . . this ambiguity . . . gives idle talk the semblance of having everything decided in it.' Ambiguity cannot be avoided, as people are 'thrown' into a world of 'being-with-another', the world of the anonymous 'they'.[86]

Heidegger insists that people must not remain lost in the 'they', but must find their true selves, their possible authenticity. This potentiality is attested by the 'voice of conscience' which:

has the character of an *appeal* [for people to realize their true selves] . . . If in this lost hearing, [the hearing which one 'loses' by 'failing to hear'] one has been fascinated with the 'hubbub' of the manifold ambiguity which idle talk possesses in its everyday 'newness', then the call [of conscience] must do its calling without any hubbub and unambiguously, leaving no foothold for curiosity.

In that way conscience provides true understanding.[87] Authenticity is ultimately tested by one's attitude towards one's death. 'One says, "death certainly comes, but not right away". With this "but . . .", the "they" denies that death is certain . . . The "they" covers up what is peculiar in death's certainty – *that it is possible at any moment.*' Heidegger reminds us that by being thrown into the world we have already been delivered to our death. We are true and authentic if we accept our death freely, 'released from the illusions of the "they".'[88]

Humanity as a body is affected by the mentality of the anonymous crowd, but individuals, as Heidegger rightly insists, have the freedom and the duty to save themselves from the collective inauthenticity. Can a person also preserve his or her selfhood in the face of the corporate social-historical situation under which they live? Can they avoid being sucked into the social spiritual malaise which, as we discussed in chapter 1, was eloquently described by Richard Sennett and his colleagues? We must assume that such freedom exists, that people can confront and overcome the danger of their denigration. We thus disagree with Sartre who claimed that the:

> class encumbrances can be seen variously as the passive synthesis of materiality, the crystallized praxes of preceding generations, the general conditions of social activity, the most immediate and brutal aspects of our objective reality, its predetermination in general.

We also disagree with an application of this fatalistic philosophy:

> The life-course of a worker at Dop Shampoos, even down to the fantasies of the machinist, is predetermined in general. The factory girl, in her sexual relations, pregnancies, abortions, *realizes* by herself what she is *already*. She passes against herself the sentence already passed by the whole nexus of socio-economic conditions into which she has been born.[89]

The rejection of this predeterminism follows from our affirmation of the twofold freedom 'to set at a distance' not only our environment, which includes our social-economic situation, but also ourselves (*see* page 4), which means that, after having realized the implications, we can refuse to accept a mentality as binding which is *incompatible* with the image of our true self.

GUILT

If we fail to realize these freedoms, our conscience pronounces us guilty. We are also guilty if we fail to meet a challenge to our selfhood when we are confronted by somebody else. Karl Jaspers has provided an illustration of such a falsehood: if a friend who knows your situation well appeals to you to make the vital decision which is necessary to save your integrity, he or she acts as the voice of your conscience. You are guilty if you fail to respond to this call. Your excuses may take different forms. Jaspers mentions stubbornness: 'I am too old to change my way of doing things', or 'people have to accept me as the person I am', or 'my nerves are too bad'. If the friend persists in confronting you with your duty, your guilty excuses may escalate: 'I can't take it', 'this is unbearable', 'I shall suffer a nervous breakdown'. There is the possibility that self-denigration may be your defence: 'I am unworthy, good for nothing, do with me what you like (knowing that it is up to you to do the right thing)'. Finally, you can cut short your friend's well-intentioned efforts: 'You can't expect of me that I discuss this matter with you', or 'I object to your interference.'[90]

Conscience calls on people to be true to themselves; a guilty conscience pronounces them to be false. which causes a deep disturbance. They have lost confidence in themselves and cannot trust themselves in their decisions. When meeting their fellow human beings they feel that they will not be trusted by them. They are liable to become lonely, anxious, depressed figures.

GUILT MEMORIES

People's minds return to the occasion or occasions when they failed to act responsibly. The German philosopher Max Scheler has provided an account of two ways in which people had such memories, with different consequences for their mental health. The account is holistic. Not only does it consider the whole person, but also the whole stretch of a human life as a crucial factor. Scheler's investigation is of basic importance in the understanding of spiritual holism and the treatment of those who suffer from a holistic breakdown.

Scheler's first type has a fixed mind. The attention of such people remains fixed to the past where, they feel convinced, they went wrong. Scheler considers that some are too proud to admit that they ought to change. Others are afraid to contemplate a development because they would not be able to recognize themselves any more.

The second type is dynamic. These people have the chance of a new beginning, but it can only be achieved if they repent first. They have realized fully their guilt. 'Repentance eliminates the root of the guilt and thus opens a new beginning'.[91] It is not just a matter of having good intentions; what is required is the strength to carry out such resolutions. This power will be made available if a new person has been born who does not continue the earlier trend. In Scheler's words, the act of repentance means that people have climbed to a higher moral level and they see below the former constitution of their ego.[92] In this way their guilt has enabled them to manifest their freedom.

If guilty people do not move towards the establishment of self-confidence when they can accept themselves again, there is the danger that the movement occurs towards self-destruction, people taking revenge upon themselves for what they believe they deserve as punishment. They 'wallow' in their guilt.[93]

Dorothy Rowe considers that those who feel guilty of having avoided life's challenges may take refuge in depression which provides them with the safety of an enclosure. Although the place is uncomfortable, it is safe and no demands are made on them.[94] It is obvious that they gain their freedom only if they feel guilty because they have escaped into the prison of their depression.[95] Their conscience reminds them of that guilt.

FALSE GUILT

False guilt is unjustified guilt. For instance, a girl may have been made to feel guilty by her mother who has dominated her and who has insisted on submission. It is the mother who is guilty. She may express her wrong demands by saying, 'When you were a child, I did everything for you. Now you ought to repay your debt and devote yourself entirely to me.' The daughter's reply ought to be in words such as 'It was your duty, mother, to look after me when I was a child. Now my duty is to devote my energies to establishing myself as a person in my own rights. In addition I shall try to help you.'

An emotional illness can cause irrational feelings of guilt in patients who suffer from compulsive thoughts and actions. They feel guilty if they do not comply with their urge, for instance, to touch a certain object a fixed number of times, as not to do so would endanger the life of a loved person. Such people know that they are wasting their lives by obeying the call for the ritual. Their duty consists of trying to find a cure for their illness.

Finally, there is the false guilt of patients who suffer from severe depression, accusing themselves of having committed all sorts of crimes. These imaginary criminal deeds have no basis in reality. Once the depression lifts, the feelings of guilt vanish.

An ethic which relies on the voice of conscience must concern itself with the falsehood of an escape into the anonymity of the crowd and must accept the judgement of guilt. But it must also take into account the results of mental illness and therefore must admit the possibility of false guilt. In order to sustain a claim of universal validity, the ethic must prove that it is accepted by people in general, although they may not be aware of their acceptance.

TACIT ACCEPTANCE OF THE TRUE-SELF ETHIC

A vital choice involves a test for the exercise of personal freedom and constitutes the hallmark of a true person. It means that people have to face the possibility of having made the wrong decision. Their conscience pronounces guilt only if they have acted hastily, without consideration of the consequences of their action, or if their motives were morally wrong. They also feel guilty if they unduly delay their decision, as that means that they are lacking in courage. Many weak people suffer agonies in such situations and their torments prove that they tacitly acknowledge the true-self ethic, as they feel prevarication to be false.

Life imposes tests that nobody can avoid. Even with conscientious management, a business person may face bankruptcy because of an economic crisis in the country; people may lose their jobs although they have worked diligently; the outbreak of war may completely disrupt people's lives. For many people the worst calamity is when they lose a loved-one through death. In all such exigencies their conscience demands that life's challenges should be met. What is at stake is people's self-esteem, without which they cannot face themselves as true persons. Even if one has been spared any such trials, one trial remains − that of facing severe illness and death. A case study that illustrates how the true self is tested is given below.

TESTS IMPOSED BY ILLNESS AND DEATH

A BATTLE WITH CANCER

Cornelius Ryan battled with cancer for four years and described his fight in a book which was compiled from extensive notes and tapes, and edited and partly written by his widow.[96] The moving drama forms part of a study by Anne Hawkins, an American lecturer,[97] and her account will be followed. As the title of the book, *A Private Battle*, indicates, Ryan, who suffered from adenocarcinoma of his prostate gland, took an aggressive stance. He was working on a historical book about the Second World War when he first learnt about his disease. His aim was to complete his book before his life ended.

Ryan fought his illness as an enemy might be fought in a war. 'Cancer is regularly thought of as an alien intruder, silent destroyer, creeping death, invading enemy' and the treatments are 'similarly militaristic, whether the treatment is surgical excision of cancerous tissue, bombarding the cancer with radiation, or fighting it with chemotherapy'.[98]

In this war, the doctors are skilled 'tacticians', the 'enemy' may make unpredictable movements and the helpful friends are courageous civilians of the Resistance. Ryan sees himself as commander-in-chief, while his physicians are other generals with whom he consults, planning the battle. 'In the end, he figures as one of the many brave and courageous soldiers who die fighting.'[99]

In order to fight his war and to gain the necessary knowledge, Ryan conducted research into cancer. *A Private Battle* consists of many skirmishes, remission means a temporary success, relapse a victory for the enemy. 'Courage is at its peak when one has run out of hope. A soldier figures he has nothing to lose because subconsciously he has arrived at the conclusion that he has no future.'[100] Ryan recorded a second great battle which was between his disease and his wish to finish his historical book. This battle was won, as Ryan died one month after his book had been completed.

Seeing himself as a courageous soldier helped Ryan to bear the pain of his illness with dignity, to endure the side-effects of the operation and the drugs which changed his body so that it had similarities to a woman's – enlarged breasts and a female pubic hair pattern. He became sterile and impotent. His self-respect was further undermined by incontinence, confinement to a wheelchair, and the disfiguring obesity produced by steroid drugs. This was felt as a 'symbolic assault on his masculinity'.[101]

When Ryan realized that the cancer had spread to other parts of his body, he knew that he could not 'win his battle'. Now his aim was to show courage, pride, compassion and heroism. His compassion goes out to fellow soldiers in the battle against cancer, one of them a young woman, screaming in pain, watched by her husband and daughter. Ryan 'maintains his defiant resistance to the very end. Just before undergoing surgery he tapes a last message to his family, where he acknowledges and accepts the possibility of death, maintaining that he is not afraid, and then adds that he intends to resist dying with all the resources he can muster, commenting wryly that his resistance to death will extend even to God: "I will dispute the Man Upstairs about it – if I have to".'[102]

According to the writer of the paper, Ryan became a vehicle of transcendence which enabled him, a sick and dying man, to achieve a 'measure of dignity and nobility'.[103] He thus realized a full measure of his true self.

ENDURING ANGINA PECTORIS

The account of the bodily experience of this excruciatingly painful condition is given in an autobiography by France Pastorelli, which was first published in France in 1933.[104] It is likely that today such suffering could be much more efficiently relieved by modern drugs. The account is quoted to illustrate how Pastorelli experienced her illness and how she attained her true selfhood in relation to her suffering.

Madame Pastorelli was a highly gifted concert pianist. Up to the age of 20 she was in good health, but then she started to suffer from a painful constriction across her chest whenever she exerted herself, including playing the piano. She married young and suffered her first serious attack in the second year of her marriage. Although she was informed by a professor of medicine that she could expect to live only for another few months and not more that one year, her account spans 15 years after her first attack.

Like Ryan, she speaks of a 'hard battle', but not so much against her illness, but 'against bodily weakness'. Having experienced signs of recovery, which proved to be misleading, she felt 'condemned to immobility like a tree rooted in the ground'.[105] The attacks occurred more and more frequently, adding to her fatigue and making her realize that 'my malady would last as long as myself . . . I at last understood, what every fibre of my being rebelled against, namely, that the malady which had seized me would not lose its hold, any more than a vulture would relinquish the prey gripped in beak and claw.'[106]

Madame Pastorelli came to understand that although sickness restricts life, it can also broaden it and be fruitful. 'A physical weakness can be transformed by a vitalizing thought into a particular kind of force, which goes on increasing in dynamic power.'[107] Her illness led her to a discovery: 'I had to blaze a lonely trail, and rebuild by myself'.[108] For carrying out this task, she found that some hidden powers gave her strength which she did not know she possessed.

Madame Pastorelli was sustained in her spiritual striving by her deep Christian faith, but she was sure that without such faith a patient's life can still be spiritually transformed. Her path was lonely, but she was aware also of her surroundings even if people failed to understand her needs. 'At the beginning of an illness one makes the mistake of thinking that if one's trouble is described it will be made intelligible. Later one learns that whether one speaks of it or not, it will still be impenetrable to the onlooker.'[109] By understanding her true self, she gained her freedom in contemplation 'which gives to the active life of a being its fullness and fruitfulness', and was able to love 'which was always undergoing purification and increase'.[110]

COPING WITH A STROKE

A different way of coping with the experience of an illness has been described in *The Patient*, a novel by Georges Simenon.[111] Although the hero is a fictional character, the experience is described with great insight into the particular illness borne by a particular character. The hero is René Maugras, a powerful newspaper proprietor, who, at the age of 54, while dining with friends, suffered a stroke. He was transferred to a hospital where he regained consciousness.

> His limbs were moving aimlessly, at random, uncontrolled. Then he tried to call out, to shout for help. His mouth opened wide, but no sound came out of it. His body was bathed in sweat, his forehead was damp, and yet he felt cold, his whole body was shaking uncontrollably.[112]

During the first stage of this illness, René did not care, but gradually he noticed what was going on around him. He discovered that half of his body was paralysed, but he was still indifferent to the way he was being treated, fed intravenously. In his helpless state Maugras was washed by his nurse and felt ashamed of his 'lumpish figure' which used to worry him in his youth.[113] Before he had suffered his stroke, his desire to be an important person had made him indifferent to his physical appearance. His illness had changed that indifference. When he was persuaded to speak and could only 'bleat: "Mon-sieur"' he felt angry and near to tears'.[114] He thought calmly about his death. The world seemed meaningless and he felt that he did not belong to it. But his helpless state made him review his past:

> What had been the point of working so hard to learn things he could never assimilate, since he was to leave school before his final examination? . . . What was the point of living? . . . He had experienced the same sense of emptiness, even when he was making the greatest efforts and achieving the most tangible success. . . . Was the effort of living really worth while? Living for the sake of what?[115]

He did not care to see the flowers which were sent to him, and he did not want to see the cards that accompanied the flowers.

Maugras' uncaring attitude alarmed his doctors. They wanted his co-operation, but it was not forthcoming as he was depressed and expected either to die or to become a permanent invalid. Maugras found the cheerful approach of his doctors, their breathing optimism, unacceptable. He not only suffered from the illness, he had to endure additional suffering from the treatment. In order to clear his air passages of the mucus which could lead to pneumonia, he was held down, his jaws were forced apart and a tube was thrust down his throat. A pump was attached to it and he felt that his lungs were sucked out. Then rubber tubes were introduced into his nostrils in order to clear his nasal passages. The patient felt that his brain was being removed.

> They had hurt him badly, and above all they had frightened him badly. And they had taken away the little confidence he had left in himself, and in the potentialities of man . . . He had been held down on his bed by alien hands. He had been merely a terrified animal. If he could have bitten them he would have done so. And that made him unhappy.[116]

Maugras' mood changed: from feeling vindictive and furious at having been held down forcibly, he now felt resentful of his own panic. He blamed himself because he had behaved like a fool and had made no effort 'to master physical suffering, to endure like a man the petty torments, to use their own terms, that they had inflicted on him'.[117]

His mood changed again and this time more profoundly. He had answered a question not by moving his head, but by saying 'No'. 'The sound had been practically normal. He was shaking with excitement.' He could say other words: 'he felt like laughing; tears were in his eyes. He had spoken! He could speak!'.[118] Maugras realized that he was making progress, but he did not want to be rushed to return to ordinary life. 'He wasn't even sure that he wanted to return.'[119] When Maugras left hospital, walking almost normally and talking fluently, he asked himself: 'Would he know to live like other people? For he was no longer quite like other people, and he never would be. Even if he had not found any answers, he had asked himself questions, too many questions perhaps, and these would always dwell within him.'[120] He renewed his intense work at his newspaper and he looked at his wife whom he had neglected during the years of his marriage. 'Yes, he would be kind [to her]! . . . Wasn't his heart brimming with kindness?' He added thoughtfully: 'If only he could have . . .' but did not finish the sentence.[121]

THE THREE BATTLES

Cornelius Ryan, France Pastorelli and René Maugras present us with examples of the innumerable experiences which patients endure. They also demonstrate that a serious sickness constitutes a challenge which people have to meet, thus realizing their freedom. Their conscience expects them to pass this test.

The pathological changes in the body arise gradually and there is first no awareness of the illness. In the cases quoted, cancerous changes in Mr Ryan's prostate, abnormalities in Madame Pastorelli's heart and in Monsieur Maugras' cerebral blood vessels were present before they declared their presence. Unaware that there is something wrong, people take their bodily health for granted. They use their bodies spontaneously to express their minds, their joys, their sorrows, their anger, their thoughtfulness or other emotions in their posture, their facial expressions and their gestures, without any awareness of their physical condition. There are bodily responses to the mental states in the skin, the heart, the digestive organs and other physical parts.

The experience of an illness disturbs the unity of the mind and body. As a spiritual exercise, the mind has to confront the body. Not only has a discomfort or pain to be faced, but the significance of the symptom has to be assessed. People have to ask themselves: is the illness serious, does it threaten my life, my work, does it mean that I shall have to call on my family and friends for support, and will they meet my needs?

The three examples revealed how each sufferer found the strength to cope with his or her particular illness, recognizing its significance as time went on. For Cornelius Ryan, it was a battle against the enemy cancer, a hostile invasion which had to be beaten back. When he realized that this battle had been lost, he decided that victory meant holding back the final defeat, death, until he had finished his book. He won that battle and, through his courage, a battle against a moral collapse.

For Madame Pastorelli, a fight against the forces that caused the agonizing pain in her chest was impossible. Instead, her battle was against any resentment and withdrawal from her surroundings. She conceived her suffering as a test for her spiritual – religious faith and certainly succeeded in that fight.

Monsieur Maugras' case is different. As the brain was the diseased part, and the mind depends on the brain, his mind was not free to confront the experience while his brain was not functioning normally. Thus, even when he regained consciousness he was dazed, then indifferent, as he could not summon the strength to fight. Later he rebelled against the administrations of his doctors, but eventually overcame his feelings. His true self also manifested itself when he took stock of his attitude towards the values which had dominated his strivings in the past. He changed as a result of having suffered the stroke. Moreover, he became more tolerant and caring towards his wife.

DEATH

Death is the ultimate test which people have to face. Here is the freedom which was emphasized by Martin Heidegger (*see* pages 44–45). Many people pass through a number of stages before they can accept the fact that their lives are finished. Dr Elizabeth Kübler-Ross has described this development,[122] a manifestation of the true self.

Doctors must face the dilemma of whether patients should be informed of the fatal nature of their illness. Some years ago medical practitioners would tell the nearest relative the exact position, while the patient was not told. This attitude has largely changed and many patients are now faced with the truth, assuming that they have the strength to cope with this knowledge. Such openness can make relations between the family and friends and the dying person easier.

There is often a prolonged struggle before seriously ill people will accept the truth. Initially, they will deny that there is no hope of recovery. At that stage, all hope should not be taken away. Anxious questions regarding the outcome of the illness should not receive a complete answer, but it should be stressed that the condition is very serious.

While sick people are not yet ready to die but suspect the worst, many express great anger and protest against their fate: 'Why should this happen to me? You people are so much more fortunate.' They may insult their nurses and complain about the treatment and the food. These insults should not be taken personally and lead to a withdrawal from the dying person. The attacks must be understood as a sign of despair. The rage has to be faced by the patients so that it can be overcome. The relatives of the dying may show anger as well – for instance, mothers of dying children.

After the initial anger there will be peace, but that peace may be interrupted by bargaining, perhaps with God: 'Can I not have at least some more months?' Gradually, there is just grief and mourning over the loss of life. Patients may cry and should be allowed to experience their sadness. The final stage is when the person is at peace, detached from life. At that point death has been accepted and no effort should be made to encourage the taking of food nor should drugs be used to prolong life. Scientific tests are also out of place. Dr Kübler-Ross expresses such patients' needs and their contribution to those around them in words which sum up the true nature of selfhood, faced with death:

> The final loving care of the dying patient is a subtle art we have to teach the medical student . . . No one better than a dying patient will help *us* to come to peace with our finiteness. If we spend a little time with them, if we can *hear* them when *they* are ready to talk, they will teach us not only what it is like to be dying, but also essential lessons in living![123]

How far is science relevant in understanding dying? It is impersonal and cannot deal with the individual. Science is interested in such universal factors as religion and ethnic belonging. A paper in a psychiatric journal which reports on communicating with dying cancer patients in India provides an example of how individual and universal factors in this field are evaluated by the scientific and the spiritual-holistic points of view.

The authors of the paper stress some points which the followers of the true-self ethic can accept: they state that the news of the nature of the fatal illness should be broken in different ways according to the patient's personality and intelligence. These factors are, of course, individual. The role of religious faith is also assessed in a manner which the true-self ethic can accept: Indians in general can cope with the thought of death more easily than members of countries which have no or different religious beliefs, because Indians accept the soul as immortal and its transfer in reincarnation. Furthermore, the close family ties, characteristic of Indian communities, are helpful when patients face their imminent death.

But true selfhood cannot be expressed in answer to routine structured questionnaires which ask such questions as 'What was your reaction when you came to know about the diagnosis? Did you become very serious? Very anxious? Did you feel dejected?'. It does not help to know that 77 per cent of patients suffered anxiety as their predominant 'immediate emotional reaction' and that 8 per cent 'did not initially accept the diagnosis'.[124] Kübler-Ross's approach takes into account each patient's personal experience and therefore does not confront them with an interview schedule. In her communication there is room for the expression of personal grief, even for anger which, of course, is the result of anxiety, each anxiety being of a different emotional kind. Percentages which make no such differentiation provide neither correct information nor guidance for dealing with terminally ill people.

By facing the challenge of death and serious physical illness, people realize the freedom of spiritual wholeness. Doctors and other practitioners have to support patients in this enterprise by going beyond the boundaries of their scientific training. They have to be aware of the personal struggle in which sick people are engaged and must help them to come to terms with their suffering, their fate which no medical science can eliminate.

Spiritual wholeness is also manifested by those who struggle with an emotional-mental illness. As was pointed out, no science of the mind can do justice to such struggles, but a true-self psychotherapy meets this case.

4

A TRUE-SELF
PSYCHOTHERAPY

———————————— • ————————————

When people lose their partner, or a close relative or friend, they may be sustained in their grief by friends and by members of their families, but they may also require the help of a professional therapist. A true-self psychotherapy is based on the ethic of conscience and does not impose guilt on patients. It is in the nature of an appeal and leaves patients to make their own judgement about their true selfhood. As this treatment is not founded on some scientific framework, there are no interpretations which claim universal scientific truth. Therapists are not guided by a conceptual theory, but rely on their intuition to deal with their patients' problems. Thus, their practice differs, for instance, from Freudians and Jungians who explain symptoms as manifestations of the personal or archetypal collective unconscious and who raise the unconscious libidinal energy into consciousness. True-self therapists raise the unconscious conscience into consciousness, relying on their patients' tacit acceptance of this moral principle. As we agreed with Martin Buber that our moral freedom consists in our ability to 'set at a distance' not only our environment but also the forces within ourselves (*see* page 4) confrontation is the method which enables people to face their duties which are 'set at a distance' before them. A number of methods which fulfil this aim have been found applicable to individuals and groups.

METHODS

DISCUSSION

By meeting their therapist in individual sessions or in a group, patients have a chance to discover through discussion their potential true selves. They may also find out how they failed to realize their selfhood. Their early years may have been crucial when their parents, brothers, sisters and teachers played important roles in their lives. They realize that they were deprived of self-confidence because their personalities were not acknowledged and a defeatist attitude to life was engendered. Having gained this insight into their problems, the discussion can point the way to progress.

ART

The philosopher Ernst Cassirer has pointed to the significance of art for human beings, and his interpretation reveals the importance of this medium for a true-self psychotherapy. According to Cassirer, 'like all the other symbolic forms art is not the mere reproduction of a ready-made, given reality. It is one of the ways leading to an objective view of things and of human life. It is not an imitation but a discovery of reality'. [125] The gain of such an objective view is a great achievement for people who were unable to come to terms with the world and their own position in it. Cassirer further explains how art can act as a corrective for people who feel that their lives are false: 'What we call rational or scientific truth is superficial and conventional. Art is the escape from this shallow and narrow conventional world.' This does not mean that people should not face the conventional world (patients suffering from mental disturbances have to face it), but it does mean that there is a deeper, unconventional world which is of greater significance for patients. The therapeutic importance of the artistic medium is evident. For 'it is in the creativeness of art that we must seek the evidence for and the fundamental manifestation of the creativeness of life'. [126]

Patients can experience this creativeness by engaging in artistic activity. They can express their emotions in music, acting (including play reading), sculpting, painting and drawing. They may be moved by films such as *Farewell to Childhood* which portrays the difficulties of adolescence, *Preface to Life* which highlights the dangers of a possessive mother, *Roots of Happiness* which brings home the unhappy situation in an overcrowded home or *Angry Boy* which shows the violence of a child who has become a thief. Patients' imaginations may be stimulated by looking at reproductions of works of art – for instance, pictures by Chagall or Munch – or by visiting art exhibitions. Epstein's 'Madonna and Child' statue (*see* figure 1) in Dean's Mews near Cavendish Square in London makes a deep impression on many patients. The face of the Madonna expresses sadness and suffering as well as love and compassion. The child's outstretched arms and gaze represent openness to life, which makes this work of art a source

Figure 1 *'The Madonna and Child' by Sir Jacob Epstein (1880–1959)*

of comfort and encouragement. In any case, patients are encouraged to explore the significance of their own works (which need not possess any objective artistic value) or of their experiences of films, paintings or sculptures for their own emotional lives.

Dream Interpretation

In true-self treatment a dream is not considered to be a wish-fulfilment as by Freud, a re-enactment of the frustration of breast-feeding as by Klein, a visitation of an archetype as by Jung, or test for the social instinct as by Adler. The dream is a message from the unconscious conscience, a call to eliminate falsity, leading the way to true selfhood. The communication may be in a literal form, represented by some actual life situation, or in a figurative form in which symbols are used.

A dream message may help a person to find his or her true self and a way out of problems. Dreams reflect the challenge of how a person deals with his or her sexuality. Frequently dreams involve sexual organs and sexual activities. For the true-self therapist such dreams are expressions of how a person is coming to terms with his or her sexuality – one of the greatest tasks. Lonely people often dream of trying to find a companion. If a person dreams that another patient receives more attention, then he or she is experiencing jealousy and doubt. 'Does the therapist think that I can be helped?' is a very serious question which may have to be faced repeatedly by the patient who lacks confidence. Self-image is fundamental: some patients dream of missing opportunities, while others cannot find the way which leads to the right place. Disagreements with a possessive mother in a dream may herald the decision to fight for independence. Losing money may be interpreted as losing material security; when the therapist discusses this dream, the meaning of security would be the issue. A dream that involves a dangerous narrow ledge above the sea indicates the need for courage in a difficult new situation. Religious symbols in dreams call for a clarification of a person's religious faith. All interpretations of dreams must be personal to the patient, to be found by asking the patient what association with the dream comes to mind. Thus, there are no universal dream interpretations.

REVERIES

As some patients do not dream or cannot remember their dreams, and as some dreams do not provide suitable material for facing patients with their challenges, a form of confrontation has been developed which is a projection of a person's fantasy world, a reverie.

This is the method: patients either sit in a comfortable chair or lie on a couch. They are asked to shut their eyes and to relax their whole bodies. They are then told that they should imagine themselves sitting in a theatre, facing the stage. They are encouraged to relate what they see on the stage and to take part in the drama. The therapist acts as a producer and interprets, with the patients' help, the significance of the performance.

The reverie may take different forms. It may portray a current situation in a person's life, an encounter with a wife, husband, another member of the family, a friend, an employer or the therapist. The atmosphere may be friendly or hostile, reassuring or frightening. There may also be a throw-back to the past, perhaps to childhood, to unresolved conflicts which call for a solution. Strangers may appear who stand for some aspects of the patient's self. Symbolic figures in shining armour or devils may represent protective defences or malignant aggression, revealed in the patient or in another person who plays a part in that particular life. Abstract shapes may stand for smoothness or sharpness; colours may have a profound significance: gold may stand for richness, lilac for gentleness and dark red for rage. Any interpretation arises from the patient's reply to the therapist's question: what comes to your mind in relation to the particular image?

The answer gives rise to a discussion, to an elaboration of the problem and to the search for a solution. Reveries need not take place only in the consulting room; patients can produce these experiences at home and report on them at their next session. Reveries are a powerful tool which can help people to visualize and realize their true selves.

CASE STUDIES

CASE 1: A ROAD TO SELF-ASSERTION

The patient is a middle-aged married woman with two sons. She is intelligent, a capable housewife and a writer. She is highly sensitive. When she was a child, her alcoholic mother did not accept her daughter's special gifts and rejected her. Her lóving family are noisy and are unable to appreciate her needs for stillness. She feels exploited by them. She is plagued by recurrent periods of depression, severe attacks of bronchial asthma and by a terror of insanity; this fear is explained by her late father's mental illness (he died in a mental hospital) and her stepmother's thoughtless remarks telling her that she was mad.

The patient came to formulate the aim of the treatment – that she should stop being 'a walking doormat'. She gained insight into herself and was able to admit that 'her tendency was to squash herself so that she would not be squashed by others' and that if she hurt herself, she anticipated other people's hurt. Above all she realized that her asthma and depression were walls, which she built to protect herself from her family's demands. She withdrew into depression to get peace from people. She continually struggled against the idea that she should prove to be as strong as everyone else.

She found a way to recover not only from her tendency to go down with severe depression and breathlessness, but also from the falseness of her self: she learnt to assert herself. This progress was made possible as she had the freedom to confront not only the forces outside her which had to be resisted, but also the opposing forces within her. Her own words are quoted here. They mark her journey to selfhood. They also articulate her struggle to discover her true self amid conflicting tendencies. Because they represent a typical struggle for true selfhood in many phases, her poetic formulations are included at length.

SOS

Arid, withered dried up, dead,
Not feeling – not seeing,
No terror – no dread,
No passion, no emotion,
No expression, no pain,
Couldn't somebody find me?
Because I'm lost again!!
For here there is nothing,
Just an empty space,
And the mirrors of the soul
Peer out of a faceless face,
Despondency blankets a once active mind,
And the eyes that watched all
Are somehow now blind.
And the ears that once heard,
Meet with silence and hush,
And the hands once outstretched
Find nothing to touch!
And the love that encompassed
This pitiful soul,
Is now out of reach,
For this dis-spirited mole.
So isn't anyone out there looking for me?
Offering a hopeful hand to dig me free?

SELF-DESTRUCTION

This soul is self destructing!!
Just push the Panic button,
And shove this soul right off the edge,
Into Eternity.

This mind is self destructing!!
Wallowing in a darkened pit,
Just give a gentle, final push
Or boot it with a kick.

This body's self destructing,
Pushing itself beyond the limit,
Hoping it will wake sometime,
And find its Life has finished.

A Vacuum in the Midst of Contradictions

But I'm not on my own, yet I'm lonely,
For there's two of me you see,
One who is a captive, and the other half who's free.
For one of me is talking, while one of me is quiet.
One prefers the sunlight, while the other likes the dark!
One of me is open and the other 'me' is shut,
For one lives in a palace, the other a canvas hut.
One of me is happy and the other one is sad,
Could one of me be very good? and my other half
        be bad?
For one of me always listens, but the other one hears
        nought,
And one of me wants to know all things and the other
        is in doubt!
For one of me is over here and one is over there,
And one of me feels so much Hope, the other just Despair!
So if there are these two of me, which one is the 'I'?
Is it the one that always smiles or the one that always
        cries?
Is it the one that's been hurt a lot or the one too hard
        to care?
Is it the one that thinks of God? or the one who knows
        no prayer?
So which I wonder is the 'me'? the one that loves so
        deep?
Or is it the one that turns her back and even cringes in
        her sleep?
Am I the one that offers a hand ready to touch a friend?

Or am I the one who has withdrawn and which 'me'
     will win in the end?
And when will this endless conflict between 'myself'
     and 'I' and 'me'
Stop the continual battle, for all I want is serenity.
Or are we all two persons struggling from within,
Striving for the good and right and staying free from sin,
And so if I'm in this vacuum – so strange and so unreal,
Why should I be so concerned by the confusion that
          I feel . . .?

Surrounded by people – yet she was alone,
Accompanied by her family – yet on her own.
Bombarded by noise – yet nothing she heard,
Answered their questions – yet spoke not a word.
Looked at their faces and nothing she saw,
Felt so enclosed by an ever open door.
When touched on her arm – nothing she felt,
Scents wafted by her and nothing she smelt.
And when sitting or standing, she imagined she knelt,
And could not understand Life's cards that were dealt.
So she continued – yet she didn't move,
And felt no emotion so she couldn't brood.
She knew no sin – so no guilt could she feel,
For she's in a vacuum – and it isn't quite real!
Her emotions were mixed and yet she had none,
Love and hate were there – yet to her they were gone,
Liberation was near and yet she was free!
But she knew no-one – for she was me . . .

HELP AND DROWNING IN A POOL OF TEARS

There is a creature drowning in a pool of tears,
A puny, little creature with gigantic fears,
And while the creature is slowly drowning,
Someone who cared came to try to help,
But the panic-stricken creature could only whimper,
          scream and yelp!!
It couldn't take the hand that was offered, couldn't hear
          his words so calm,

Couldn't let itself be rescued for it was too deep in
        terror and alarm!
Yet this creature slowly drowning was being gently
        pulled ashore,
Because someone held the lifeline, someone who
        knew the score!
But still the creature floundered – fought against
        the rescuer's try,
And the drowning, sinking creature begged only to
        know why?
For it was drowning in its own pool of tears, completely
        bogged down by imaginary fears,
Totally unaware that it could be saved, for it feared it
        was Mad, mentally sick, afraid.
Always the fear, the creature thought it was Mad,
So it preferred to drown than be locked away so sad!
But somebody, somewhere would not let go,
And tugged at the lifeline, pulling firmly but slow!
And the creature was dragged back to the shore,
Because the one that cared wanted to prove once more,
That for the creature to drown in its own pool of tears
Allowing itself to be swamped by its fears,
Well, that wasn't the way for the creature to go,
And the caring one told the creature so,
And the bewildered creature still cowering with fright,
Still snapped and yelped and tried to fight,
And tried to lash out at those close by, and still all the
        time the poor creature cried,
But gradually through a foggy, misty, haze, the creature
        crept slowly out of its daze!!
And with eyes sore and red and emotionally drained,
Its 'loving care' lifeline had unloosened its chains,
And now, slowly so slowly perhaps this creature will find,
What it's always been seeking – complete peace of mind . . .

In her 'Welcome to Limbo Land,' the same patient expresses a phase
in her struggle to find her true self, a phase in which she describes her
withdrawal from her family and the loneliness which was the result of that
withdrawal, and her awareness of her weakness but also of her wish to
take part in life.

WELCOME TO LIMBO LAND

No depression, no despondency, but no enthusiasm nor any feeling of emotion. Nothing, just a void. Nothing can break down the invisible barrier – for it seems that I don't belong in the world anymore.

I can't be hurt now, for there is nothing left to hurt.

I can't cry now, for there are no tears.

The fear and panic are pushed away – hidden out of sight – and yet I'm not unhappy in Limbo Land. Perhaps this numbness is temporary, perhaps for good. As long as I don't hurt, then let the numbness stay!

Intense feeling of un-reality persisting. Managing menial tasks, but seem to have dis-appeared inside myself.

Putting on an act for family – ie showing modicum of enthusiasm, but it's all false. To hell with it all – I do not want to know – so if the sky falls in, then tell someone else, it's not my department.

But there is also an unmistakable loneliness as though I can no longer even communicate with those I love! I just can't be bothered – emotions drain my energy and that is already lacking.

The fragile, brittle feeling is still intense and the few times of peace and quiet when I could perhaps work things out are not helping – I start to think, and what the hell, I switch off – the numbness isn't frightening just rather weird as though I have cocooned myself inside myself and withdrawn, I can't be touched or 'got at'. It's as though it has all been too much and I have dropped out of the world completely, and yet part of me must still be here and feeling something or else I wouldn't notice the fact I feel so far removed and away from it all.

We meet the patient again 19 months later. She now defines what the reverie treatment has meant to her.

FREEDOM FROM FAMILY ENCROACHMENT

But the grey mist is more than just an escape, it is 'my place', my choice, my freedom, if only for the time being until I have all the strength I need to withstand family and business pressures.

Now I am only half-way to the summit, occasional back-slides of depression no longer cause the same amount of fear and panic as before, it may happen, it will pass. This I learn with the reverie.

I am trying to find 'me', not her idea of a daughter, not his ideal wife, not their ever-available mother – but the woman, occasionally distressed, disturbed, even emotionally distorted. But by shedding the layers under treatment, she reveals herself as a more confident, more assured and certainly more aware person.

The main problem is how to continue to accept the sensitive, vulnerable, touchy 'me' in a world of sorrow and suffering over which I have no control.

To accept that I am liable to be hurt, but no longer have a breathing problem because of it. If I am hurt there is no need to withdraw into an untouchable deep depression.

So the definition of reverie for me: a form of treatment that I little understood, a way of escape from pressure, a life-line when sinking, a time to study and learn some surprising things about myself, but most of all to find out and to know all my weaknesses and strengths. Reverie has become for me an all-important, continual lesson, facing fears and tears, horror and finding Hope . . .

Nine days later a review of the reverie yields a much more hopeful vision of her life: her favourite colour, lilac, she believes, 'will no longer feel threatened by the "mercenary factors" of her husband's business concerns'. She can be herself.

My Needs

Why ask if there is anything to take its place?

At least there I could escape occasionally and be alone for ten minutes to gather myself. At the shop there is nowhere that I can escape to – rightly or wrongly I feel that it is the same as at my mother's – slave labour for wages yet the old adage 'You only have to ask and I will buy it for you'. That is the feeling that I have.

They say that I am needed, what about *my* needs? But at least I will have Sundays free! Ten whole hours, no shop, no antiques, no auctions, no people, no family – Sundays will become a grey misty lilac heart-shaped day, and then maybe the lilac heart-shape will find a rightful place of its own and not need to soar and float above a grey mist, completely hidden from everyone else. Maybe the lilac heart-shape will no longer feel the need to be gently cradled, and will not wish to go on fluttering far away, out of reach, and into another world. Maybe it will find its peace and no longer feel threatened by the mercenary factors around it, no longer feel constricted as though life itself is being squeezed out of it, maybe!

Perhaps it will no longer need a life-line, no longer want to be 'handled only with loving care', no longer feel so hurt and vulnerable. Perhaps it will become strong to face everything and cope without crushing itself in a very, very black pit, perhaps it has never taken enough time to see into its self and face its fears, its sorrows, its loves – Sundays will be lilac heart-shaped days . . .

Case 2: Conscience Mistaken – Conscience Corrected

This is the story of a woman who described her journey to selfhood in moving language, illustrated by beautiful pictures. The story demonstrates the fallibility of the true-self therapist and the extraordinary resilience that led the patient to achieve true selfhood.

She was married, artistically gifted, capable as a wife and mother of three children. She broke down when her eldest child, a son of 20 who had been brilliant at school and had entered university with high hopes, developed schizophrenia, which meant the end of his academic career. In her despair, the mother blamed herself for not having insisted that her son should get professional help.

In a suicidal state, she was admitted to a mental hospital. 'As the wall of grief and despair got unbearable, I had felt unable to contain my destructive feelings at home.' She was given heavy drugs which upset her. Her doctor made her angry by trying to release some of her alleged aggressiveness and denying that the drugs could have the side-effects of which she complained. She described how, in her opinion, the doctor

> needs forgiving for always trying to make me angry. For saying the withdrawal effects couldn't possibly do harm. For leaving me with the only explanation I could give myself for the shivering, nausea, near black-outs, the visual disturbances, hallucinations and nightmares, that I must indeed be going mad, imagining it all, manifesting hysteria. In the end the neurologist confirmed 'withdrawal phenomenon'.

Later, she came to the conclusion that she herself

> needs forgiving for cracking up, retreating out of a situation I couldn't change, help or tolerate into the cocooned world of regressive dependency, given its ultimate expression in the ordered white-coated, rice-pudding haven of the mental hospital, an asylum life with no past, no future, just a safe present.

After her discharge from hospital, she was given further drugs which again upset her. So she started treatment with a doctor who avoided prescribing drugs and who tried to help her to discover what her conscience truly expected of her. Encouraged by the therapist, she painted a picture in which she expressed what she considered to be her guilt. She portrayed herself as a gorgon with snakes in her hair, clawing her unfortunate son's head, which was dripping with blood (*see* figure 2).

Her doctor assured her that she had no guilt. Even if psychiatric treatment had been obtained earlier, the son's illness could not have been prevented. She gained insight and wrote:

> When I first came to my new doctor, the guilt was very real. The picture of me with gorgon snake hair and claws was how I felt – that I had damaged my boy irrevocably. I don't believe that now – I had it all out of proportion, blaming and punishing myself.

Figure 2 *A patient's portrayal of herself as a gorgon to express her guilt*

Figure 3 *A depressed and bewildered patient paints herself in chains with a signpost pointing nowhere*

She remained bewildered and deeply depressed. In one picture (figure 3) she expressed her predicament in the following way: the mental hospital where she had been 'cocooned' and where she had suffered 'regressive dependency' is in the background. The members of her family who used to be her joy of giving and receiving love freely have turned into crossword-puzzle pieces which are fitted into places automatically. She herself is in chains and her signpost points nowhere. As the signs are blackened out, there is a hellish fire towards which she is being dragged.

In a another picture (figure 4) her chains are replaced by barbed wire. She is cut off from her family by a closed door. Some ghastly monsters have appeared. She herself offered the following interpretation:

> My monsters. I think there may have been anger, resentment, hatred. The breakdown put me in a very vulnerable, dependent position and because, in that condition, people, including my husband, seemed inclined to be more gentle, understanding, communicative, it became a position I may have been afraid to move out of . . . afraid, because I felt the alternative was into the

Figure 4 *The patient sees herself enmeshed in barbed wire, unable to communicate with her family*

direction of my anger and fury. I think my monsters were saying: 'they (the family) made you like this, helpless, weak, powerless, guilty – get out of it, you're really like us, strong, violent, ruthless, with sharp teeth and destructive claws. Go away. Be a person on your own. Leave them. Don't be a person defined by relationships. Don't be the prey of the great biological swindle which ensures that you feel and suffer whether you will it or not, the tug towards children whom you can't help, who seem bent on self-destruction, for whom you can only suffer and feel love. . . . Don't be hurt any more. Get rid of the chains of love, hate, destroy.' And if I moved towards them and expressed my anger, I was afraid that I would lose the newly improved tender relationship with my husband which seemed to have been brought out by my helplessness. And yet that is only a part of my nature. So I think that's why I was enmeshed in that barbed wire in that picture – forward or back were equally impossible.

Her therapist became very concerned. In one of her pictures a supporting wall was collapsing. What help could he offer? As he did not accept the 'truth' of a conceptual system whereby interpretations follow from a particular theory, he could only rely on his intuition.

He believed that the marriage situation might impede her freedom to resolve her conflict. Thus, in a monologue, he talked to her about disappointments which women have to face with regard to their husbands. His intuition was violently rejected:

Thursday the 22nd was a day that should never have happened. For all that, it started so bravely. A day with sunshine and little puffy clouds. A day when the glance of strangers met in the street and confirmed one another's existence. When travellers packed tight in the 8.35 to Victoria wryly caught one another's eyes and acknowledged the ridiculousness of their situation, and shared it. A day of meeting and not meeting. A day when the shared humanity of each creature peeping shyly from each polished face in Piccadilly seemed gloriously embodied and encompassed in the infinite love and compassion on the face of Rembrandt's *Portrait of an Elderly Man as St Paul*. A brave day. A courageous day. A day to give out, accept, become.

What does he want of her, this other old man who has travelled with her so far, for so long? 'Authenticity', he says. He has acquiesced and assented, if not actually led, in her fumbling erratic progress towards confronting the reality of her situation and relationships. He has appeared to provide an approving and safe setting where disclosures, admissions, aspirations – often in the teeth of her resistance through feelings of disloyalty and ingratitude – can come about. And he had almost succeeded. She has come in calm and content, realizing that nothing is ideal, but feeling neither cheated nor resentful. Feeling strong and sure. Ready to state the situation at last in words – and move on.

But he has misunderstood. He has replaced her face and voice with those of so many others he has seen like her. So much suffering. 'What do they want of me, these people who ask for my help and are incapable of using it?' he asks. And he begins to throw back at her what he interprets as her thoughts, but they are not hers. She is stunned. Her mirror that at last was showing a more corporeal, rosy, rounded image is clouded with misunderstanding: the horror lies beneath; and under that, once banished so she thought for ever, awaits the silent scream in the terror of the empty glass.

The tone of her protest changed. The therapist now moved into the centre:

Soon it is over. And he can draw back and observe his own thoughts and smile at so much struggling and trying. He yawns. He is very tired. It has been a long day. 'I have failed.' 'No,' she demurs, anxious to relieve him of the failure, the boredom and distaste she senses he feels. He is a very old man and a philosopher. He is becoming forgetful and a little bit deaf.

Thursday the 22nd was a day that should never have happened. Let us bury it in grateful oblivion.

The therapist could not bury the day. He was afraid that she had lost confidence in him and that she might suffer a worsening of her illness, precipitated by his misinterpretation. He was wrong again, as her next letter showed:

I thank you with all my heart. The day of the crisis, which so upset me, also freed me of dependence, because I gave you so much power and invested you with total knowledge and understanding of me. And here you were making such a gross misinterpretation; so if *you* could do that, then I obviously had to take the power (responsibility) back into my own hands, where, of course, it properly belongs and will firmly stay.

The same letter revealed some crucial insight into the origin of her breakdown and pointed the way to permanent recovery:

I think I know myself much better now. My son's illness, the violence he showed and his disappearance, as well as my husband's avoidance of the issue, were precipitating factors, but wouldn't, I think, have had such wider repercussions unless my background had made me so weak in this area.

The insecure child was compensating by over-achievement and 'super-goodness' as a charm to ward off rejection. *I could not fail.* The wrong sort of pride was there too. The more people marvelled at what I did, the more it fed my determination. They said things like, 'I don't know how you do *half* of what you do.' I would grit my teeth and do even more, and pretend it was nothing – that my determination would make everything run smoothly, turn out alright.

I was in despair over my son. Here was something I couldn't make alright. He was beyond reach, love, hope, help. He became my failure, my guilt. Still pride – whatever went right or wrong had to be a result of *me* operating on it. The powerlessness over my boy, my husband's avoidance, his closure of communicating channels, but reaching out for sex, all took root in the fertile ground of my inner fears and confirmed the unacknowledged suspicion that I was a weak, powerless victim of circumstances, liable to be uprooted, sent away if unsatisfactory. So I had to be good, pretty, clever, amusing, then later mature, confident, psychologically independent – and of course it was a hollow sham (in spite of the stunning performance), a sham which my son's illness, my unmet need for support from my husband exposed. I couldn't face failure as a mother.

Something has changed. I don't think I have to keep proving myself by taking on more challenges to allay the suspicion of inner inadequacy. I am human, not superhuman. I have weaknesses and failures. I am lazy, vain, proud, frivolous, opinionated, argumentative – many other things – and I can look at them all – it's liberating. There's not the fear, the fight between the 'is' and the 'ought'. You helped me enormously, out of the illness.

Her recovery was permanent, as the follow-up proved. The method of this treatment was by confrontation. She admitted:

I think the most helpful thing you have done with me is to keep asking me 'why' and what things stand for. Being afraid of being depressed is silly. It's the fear that is perpetuating both itself and depression. I can now look at what I feel, accept what the feeling is, try to find out why I feel it. It's less likely to bring on panic, anxiety, agitation, etc.

Thus, the last picture (figure 5) shows her happy, with her husband and the family dog carrying the hopeful message between its teeth.

This patient recovered because she had gained the freedom to exchange the faulty picture of herself for the true picture. Her conscience had discovered the correct judgement of her duties towards herself and others. Thus, there was no longer a conflict between the 'is' and the 'ought'.

The turning point in her therapy was brought about when she violently rejected her therapist's interpretation of her marriage, couched in general terms (he had received a letter in which she had confronted critically the relationship with her husband). Out of this anger arose the strength to look at her whole life in a new and healthy manner.

Figure 5 *Fully recovered after treatment, the patient portrays herself in a happy, hopeful situation*

CASE 3: RECOVERY FROM FACELESSNESS

A married woman, the mother of a little girl, complained of depression. No clue could be found in the current circumstances of her life. Her training at an art school was considered as a possible help to provide an explanation of her illness. She was asked therefore, to draw two pictures, one of herself and the other of the therapist. In that way, it was hoped, some light might be thrown on the way she saw herself and the world around her.

The result was startling: neither she nor the therapist had a face. There was only the outline of their heads, the rest was blankness (*see* figure 6a).

Looking at these portraits, she realized that she wore a mask when meeting people, but that there was a face behind this concealment. She and her therapist now discovered why she was depressed.

The next task was to find out how this apparent lack of a personality had come about. She attributed the void within herself, manifesting in her facelessness, to her mother's influence. She had dominated her life and also tried to prevent her marriage. As the patient did not feel that she had

Figure 6 (a–d) *Recovery from facelessness*

a face, she could not see faces in other people. Her world was empty, depressed.

But this feeling was misleading, for it was a false self which experienced the emptiness, and there was a true self behind the façade, awaiting release. Two forces were being mobilized in its liberation.

The first was the relationship with the therapist. Whereas the patient's mother never acknowledged her as a person, he did. He opened her eyes to an understanding of mother's influence on her life, and he also induced her to engage the second force, her artistic gift.

Although the pictures are depressing, they are her works of art and, in the words of the philosopher Ernst Cassirer already quoted on page 58, they reveal her reality which is not only her illness but also her creative means of recovery.

With the therapist's encouragement a further picture was drawn. Now there is a face, full of expression, but it is not yet her own, the face of a mature woman. It is the face of a child, looking depressed, with pent-up emotion (figure 6b). Thirteen days later, her face is that of a rather anxious grown-up (figure 6c), to be followed four and a half weeks later by the contour of a mature person (figure 6d). Although she is still thoughtful, her emotions are now freer and there is a faint smile on her face.

Two months later, she reported that she was able to organize a big party as a surprise to celebrate her father's eightieth birthday and she admitted that she could not have managed such a thing before the treatment. Her mother was present at the party and the patient bore her no grudge.

CASE 4: GROWTH STUNTED BY MOTHER'S NEGLECT

In spite of her mother's domination, the last patient had the basis of a fulfilled life as a wife and mother. Such a basis did not exist in the case of a single young woman, the youngest of seven children who felt that her mother had only loved her brothers and sisters, but not her. In her picture (figure 7) she portrayed herself as a stunted tree, overshadowed by the other trees which deprive her of the chance to grow.

Her own interpretation of her situation was as follows:

There is love between my mother and her other children. That gives them the strength to live and they move on, while I am rooted in fear and bitterness. I can't even rise from my bed, can't get the strength to go out to work, go out into the world, not even to the shops. Mother's love is their food, primal food. That is what I must get before I can feed my flesh and blood. I have cried for this love in vain, my chest aches with melancholia. My hope is getting fainter and fainter. Instead, there is a load of vile, fiendish feelings and utterances, my love is turning into hate.

The therapist was unable to help this stunted personality to grow. This patient had not enough strength to come to terms with her situation. She remained depressed and sought refuge in drink.

Figure 7 *Deprived of her mother's love, the patient portrays herself as a stunted tree, overshadowed by the other trees, representing her six brothers and sisters*

Case 5: Liberation from Mother's Hatred of Men

A married woman of 42 asked for help because she had been depressed for the last two years. Her doctor prescribed an anti-depressant drug which masked her symptoms but left her unfit to carry out her work as a lecturer and which had also made her frigid.

The depression started when she discovered that her husband was unfaithful. The news left her 'devastated'. The sexual part of the marriage had never been satisfactory. Twenty years earlier they had married because she became pregnant. Ever since she felt resentment against her husband who 'forced' her into the marriage. She had two daughters.

She admitted to her therapist that her husband's infidelity had at least partly been her fault, as she had rejected him. He felt guilty about the affair with the other woman. He had always found his wife attractive, but he had become tired of the situation at home and had been quite angry at times. He needed more understanding from his wife, especially with regard to his professional problems.

The husband now presented the patient with a remedy: why not pay him back by having an affair with a mutual friend who had indicated that he would be very willing to oblige?

When the therapist was asked to give his opinion about this 'cure' for the patient's depression, he asked her whether she herself would feel that such action would be right. Her conscience decided against it and the plan was abandoned.

She then presented the therapist with a contradictory statement: 'I don't deserve to be happy, but I have a right to happiness.' This ambiguity pointed to a conflict and its resolution was considered to be crucial. A reverie provided the clue: she relived the sexual pleasure she experienced when her husband had intercourse with her 20 years earlier. But such pleasure was forbidden according to her mother who had instilled a hatred of men into her after she herself had endured an unhappy marriage for which her husband was blamed. Thus the patient could not allow herself any enjoyment with a man. When she discovered her pregnancy, she first refused to have anything further to do with her husband, testing his love. However, he passed the test and offered to marry her. Her parents did not attend the wedding because they felt that she had 'let them down'. The neighbours were not informed about the pregnancy.

She discovered that she could love her baby. When her second child was born, her husband started an affair with another woman. She did not find out, however, until two years ago, when her depression started.

The road leading to recovery from her illness and to her true selfhood now lay open. Her mother's pernicious influence had to be eradicated because it was an imposition which had distorted her opinion of men.

In order to make the break from her mother's power easier, her therapist suggested that she should change her Christian name which, of course, was chosen by her mother. A new name was chosen and she gradually identified herself with a woman with normal sexual needs who is lovable by her husband. She lost the resentment she felt against him for so many years and consequently lost her depression. The relationship with her husband was now satisfactory and she resumed her teaching, which was good for her self-esteem. A follow-up consultation confirmed her recovery. The total number of consultations was 17.

CASE 6: RECONCILED TO MOTHER

A middle-aged woman had a dream which showed her a way of accepting her mother whom she had always felt had failed her, which she resented: 'I dreamt that I was in a children's playground on a sort of roundabout, standing up while my mother was standing below on the ground.' The therapist interpreted this scene as referring to the patient's active life in contrast to her mother's whose life is no more in full swing. The dream went on: 'Mother asked me to help her to join me, but I told her that I would never do so because she had been so cruel to me and had made me suffer so much when I was a child.' At that point the daughter discovered the chance of a new relationship with her mother which was in accordance with her conscience and her true self: 'All at once I realized that she would die if I didn't help her. So I picked her up in my arms. She had become suddenly small and limp and I carried her in my arms like a lifeless baby.' The mother had ceased to be a dominant, threatening, cruel figure, her 'lifelessness' was now grasped: she had had a tragic life when young, a terrible childhood. Her father had died when she was only four years old, her emotional life was strangled, and hence she was unable to give love to her children.

Reconciliation in this case could not be expected to last – the mother disappointed the daughter again. The challenge consisted of coming to terms with the mother's unloving personality and no longer expecting signs of love from her. This did not mean that the mother was entirely indifferent to her daughter. For instance, she might show signs of deep concern if the daughter were taken seriously ill. In the treatment, the daughter had to realize her mother's emotional weakness and her own great need for affection which her mother could not meet. The daughter was the mother of two children herself. She divorced her husband as she felt that he did not love her and care for her. She gave her children all the attention she was capable of, but had to endure their lack of love for her on many occasions. But there were also times when both her son and daughter demonstrated their fondness for her. Such a case illustrates that we can never make ultimate judgements about people's feelings for one another. There is thus not a static true or false self. There are many fluctuations when doubts have to be faced and when a person's conscience has to be reassured, the voice saying: 'I have done for my children [or my mother] what I was able to do at the time.'

CASE 7: DIGGING UP THE TREASURE OF FEMININITY

A single woman, aged 37, received a dream message which confirmed the need to change important aspects of her life. She had been successful in an academic career, had a few women friends, but no relations with men. Her elderly parents, weakened by physical illnesses, had always provided a safe setting for her life. As the result of her therapy, she concluded that she must make a decisive change. Her dream was as follows.

She was digging up a treasure which was in the shape of a crate into which wine bottles could be fitted. She associated the treasure with her femininity. Later she dreamt that she was sitting at a meal table with her parents. The meal, however, was tasteless. The interpretation was that the 'fare' which they had provided had lost its attractive flavour and that she was now ready to taste a life with a man in its many aspects, symbolized by the many sections in the crate.

It was obvious that this 'treasure' would not be 'dug up' quickly. The patient was faced with years during which she was searching for a male companion. As her social life failed to provide her with opportunities for meeting suitable men, she advertised and also joined an organization that put women in touch with suitable men.

During her therapy, many such encounters were faced. She met men who, being of the same age, were not committed to enter into any permanent relationship which she needed to be her true self. She experienced sexual–erotic encounters; although they ended in disappointments, they did develop her feminity. She discovered that some men, usually about ten years older than herself, after a failed marriage looked to her as support for their particular emotional problems, without considering her own needs. While she made a great effort to satisfy the demands made by one of them, she gave up the relationship after he had bluntly refused to provide her with a child. Her therapist pointed out to her that her experience was typical for women of her age and that she could express her situation creatively as a professional writer.

GROUP TREATMENT

While the same method of confrontation which is employed in individual true-self psychotherapy is employed in the treatments of groups, the ethic is now concerned with doing justice not only to one self but also to the other selves who form the group. This new situation requires a consideration of the factors which operate between people. The third part of this book has been reserved for this subject.

For the therapist the question is how much help patients should receive from the treatment. The answer depends on how able and how motivated they are to respond to the confrontation with the demands of their true selves. Whatever may be the results in individual cases, the validity of the ethical principle is not in question. This became evident from the earlier discussion that people have to pass crucial tests when they make vital decisions or when they face severe illness or death. Thus, there is a tacit universal acceptance of the true-self ethic, but it is necessary to articulate its truth in view of our social spiritual malaise which is manifest in the widespread suffering from mental disorders and the frightening epidemic of drug addiction. There is therefore a need to elucidate our spiritual existence.

CONCLUSION OF PART I

———————————— • ————————————

OUR SPIRITUAL EXISTENCE

The ethical principle of the freedom of the true-self personality is founded on the presupposition of man's spiritual dimension. This dimension, however, is usually considered to be restricted to his religious faith. This amounts to an insult to those who have no such faith, as they would be denied a share in the realm of personal moral freedom and the search for meaning. This realm is in a spiritual crisis. It affects Christians and those who have no religious faith. Kierkegaard, himself a devout Christian, focused on one aspect of this crisis by emphasizing the problem of reconciling faith and reason on the 'tension between a sceptical mind and a religious heart'.[127] For Kierkegaard this problem represents the essence of human existence and he became the founder of a philosophy called existentialism. Several modern thinkers who are mainly concerned with a person's responsibility when making a choice, are classed existentialists.

David E Roberts, a philosopher of religion, has summarized existentialist views and by so doing has provided an account of the forces which promote and those which oppose the acceptance of the true-self ethic. According to Roberts, existentialism is firstly:

> a protest against all forms of rationalism which find it easy to assume that reality can be grasped primarily or exclusively by intellectual means. It is an emphatic denial of the assumption that construction of a logical system is the most adequate way to reach the truth.[128]

This protest is shared by those who uphold the true-self ethic and who reject the claim that a scientific truth, based on the construction of an intellectual, rational and logical system, can grasp the truth of the reality of a human being.

In the second place, existentialism is a protest against all views which tend to regard man as if he were a thing, that is, only an assortment of functions and reactions. This means that in the sphere of philosophical theory, existentialism stands against mechanism and naturalism [the view according to which only the operation of natural as opposed to supernatural and spiritual laws and forces is assumed]; and in the sphere of social theory it stands against all patterns of human organization in which the mass mentality stifles the spontaneity and uniqueness of the individual person.[129]

The followers of the true-self ethic join in this protest which endorses the rejection of the reflexological theory of behaviour therapists, the Freudian or Jungian theories, according to which individual people are turned into libidinal or archetypal objects, the Gestalt theory which reduces human relations to quasi-biological functions, the Alderian theory of the social interest which denies the uniqueness and freedom of the individual, and the Sartrian theory according to which all people are predetermined by their socio-economic nexus. Stifling of the true self is inevitable in a scientific theory which, as we learn from the former Oxford Professor of Philosophy, R G Collingwood, is by its very nature mechanistic, imposing its 'abstract law ignoring the omnipresent individuality of the real'.[130]

A neurological, impersonal, mechanistic pharmacological application which leads to the discovery of psychotropic drugs is completely justified if such treatment is needed by patients who, because of their mental illness, have no freedom to realize their true selves. As objects of science, treated with such drugs, they are saved from suffering and they may even regain their moral freedom as the result of such therapy. But the very image of a person must not be conceived in neurological or any other scientific terms.

Roberts's third interpretation of existentialism clarifies another vital aspect of the true-self ethic: 'Thirdly, existentialism makes a drastic distinction between subjective and objective truth, and it gives priority to the former against the latter.' Here he is not concerned with the subjective in the sense of being biased, prejudiced or unreliable, nor does he deny the value of objectivity in science, common sense or logic. What existentialists

insist [is] that in connection with ultimate matters it is impossible to lay aside the impassioned concerns of the human individual. They are calling our attention to the fact that in the search for ultimate truth the whole man, and not only his intellect or reason, is caught up and involved. His emotions and his will must be aroused and engaged so that he can live the truth he sees . . . [He is then] *being grasped* by the truth in a decisively personal manner.

Although feelings, hopes or fears or any other emotions can be stated objectively,

> the subjective point of view puts the individual with his commitments and passions in the very center of the picture. And only by the latter approach, say the existentialists, can a man be so grasped and changed inwardly as to deepen and clarify his relationship to reality, even as a thinker.[131]

This interpretation confirms and explains the value of the true-self psychotherapy in which patients are involved with their subjective commitments and passions in their efforts to discover their true selves in communication with their therapist through the medium of discussion, art, dream interpretation and reveries.

Roberts lists a fourth existentialist characteristic: the human situation is seen as

> filled with contradictions and tensions which cannot be resolved by means of exact or consistent thinking . . . [man's] whole life is enmeshed within a natural and social order which profoundly and inevitably determines him . . . [but] he must himself create the answer [to his determination] by using his freedom.[132]

According to the true-self ethic, people will realize their freedom by *confronting* the natural and social order so that they are no longer enmeshed in it.

PART II

———————————— • ————————————

BIOLOGICAL HOLISM

5

INTERPRETATIONS OF BODILY WHOLENESS

———————————— • ————————————

BODILY CHALLENGES

Human spiritual existence involves the body. As discussed in chapter 3, a bodily illness, especially if it is grave or terminal, presents sufferers with the spiritual challenge of coping with their distress. In all such cases patients' selfhood is tested and this applies also to people like the asthmatic woman discussed in chapter 4 who discovered under treatment that she had used her disease as an escape from her domestic situation which she learnt to face without such evasion.

The subjective side of human wholeness, stressed by David Roberts, is relevant for an understanding of the part which the body plays in it. It expresses people's emotions of joy, fear and sadness by means of such functions as digestion, breathing, the circulation, including the heart, and in the condition of the skin which changes from a blush to pallor, from dryness to perspiration.

The body presents a further challenge to our moral freedom: this is evident from Roberts's fourth existential characteristic − a person's determinativeness by the natural order, his biological vulnerability. Heredity plays a major role in determining fate. Some people inherit an increasing weakness of their muscles, others a combination of crippling dysfunction of their lungs, causing infections with a loss of valuable body salts through the skin. Heart disease and cancer have a genetic origin which also accounts for the quality of a person's constitution which may be weak or strong, offering the chance of a long or short life. The major mental illnesses − schizophrenia and manic-depressive psychosis − have a genetic component. All such bodily and mental suffering calls for an awareness of its spiritual significance, for the realization of spiritual freedom to meet its challenges.

Not only do people have a duty to meet the challenges of bodily illness, they also have a duty to preserve their health. This is obviously in people's own interest, but it is also in the interest of their families who will suffer if their relatives' health breaks down and who will have the burden of looking after them. People also have a duty to the community not to neglect themselves, because it is the community which will bear the cost of looking after them if they become ill.

There may be valid reasons for such neglect: a soldier in the war, a mother who wears herself out looking after her sick child, a scientist who keeps himself awake in the pursuit of knowledge – they are all inspired by a duty which is superior to their duty to health.

Although the body does not exist by itself and is always part of the whole personality, it is conceived as a whole in terms of a machine.

MACHINE-LIKE BODILY WHOLENESS

The science of the body is dominated by the image of the body as a machine. The whole structure is understood in terms of its parts and their mutual relations. As we discussed in chapter 2 with regard to the sciences of the mind, the same mechanistic conception is applied to the body. In this way, the heart, the lungs, the brain and all the other organs and the microscopic structures of which they are composed are all known not as parts of unique persons but as parts in general. Diseased bodies are known in terms of individual diseases, treated by remedies which are specific to the illnesses but not to the patients. They may be diagnosed as sufferers from appendicitis or pneumonia for which they receive the standard surgical or medical therapies. When the efficacy of a new drug is being tested, patients who are considered to be suffering from the same condition are grouped together; some receive the new remedy, while others act as a control, and receive a placebo. A statistical evaluation of the result of this comparison decides on the usefulness of the agent. Frequently there are side-effects which may affect a smaller or larger number of the treated patients and may be more or less serious. Others tolerate the drug well. This machine-like treatment is comparable to the way a motor mechanic, for instance, applies a solution to remove rust or replaces a worn-out part (which corresponds to the organ transplant technique in medicine), but there are no harmful side-effects, as cars, like all machines, have no individuality.

The science of dietetics considers the body to be a biological machine which requires food as a source of energy. Calorific requirements are assessed for people in certain occupations, at a certain age, for men, women and children, and tables are compiled which give details of the necessary energy sources. The food industry adds hundreds of non-nutritive substances and in factories food is bleached, coloured, dehydrated, hydrolysed, emulsified, gassed and chemically preserved; artificial flavouring agents are added, wholemeal flour is deprived of its outer layer which is rich in minerals and vitamins, and the valuable wheat-germ is removed. The end product is 'improved' by the use of chlorine dioxide and 'enriched' with several substances. The soil on which food is grown is treated with chemical fertilizers and crops are sprayed with toxic insecticides and herbicides.

A growing number of people distrust machine-like scientific medicine. They are concerned about the side-effects, the damage to their health and to the environment. Although drugs can relieve suffering, illnesses of the heart, blood vessels, joints and other organs only receive palliation and the total amount of disease is not getting less. But scientists have no option in their methods and one biologist, Richard Dawkins, has claimed that the mystery of life has been solved by his science. In answer to the vital question: 'What about our bodies?', the reader receives the categorical answer: 'Each one of us is a machine, like an airliner only much more complicated.'[133]

Dawkins can be refuted, however; our bodies are not machines, even if the machine conception of the body serves the purposes of medical science.

BIOLOGICAL WHOLENESS

What is at stake is the conviction that life must not be reduced to inert matter, that the integrity of a living being calls for different treatment from that which is appropriate in the case of a machine, a dead object made for a purpose by human beings. People may love their cars, but they love their plants, their pet animals or their children or other human beings in a way which differs fundamentally from the love they show to human artefacts.

In order to make his point, Dawkins is forced to use misleading images, introducing metaphors without admitting their metaphorical character; the DNA, the unit which enables biologists to account for heredity, is said to bear 'coded characters [which] spell out specific instructions[134] for building organic structures, like a foreman instructing his workmen on a building site, every cell can be thought of as a gigantic chemical factory,[135] designed and organized by a clever industrial expert'; human cells use 'only about 1 per cent of the genetic information' which is, however, 'roughly equivalent to one volume of the *Encyclopaedia Britannica*'.[136]

A well-known biologist, Paul A Weiss, has pointed out the flaw in Dawkins's argument. The error, he says, consists of endowing the DNA, the gene, with a position which cannot be claimed for it. According to Weiss, 'genes, highly organized in themselves, do not impart higher order upon an orderless milieu by ordainment, but they are themselves part and parcel of an ordered system, in which they are enclosed and with the patterned dynamics of which they interact'.[137] Thus, organic nature must not be interpreted by 'bestowing' upon the gene, understood as the unit from which the organism is built up, 'the faculty of spontaneity, the power of "dictating", "informing", "regulating", "controlling", etc the orderless processes in its unorganized milieu, so as to mould the latter into the co-ordinated teamwork that is to culminate in an accomplished organism.'[138]

As Weiss insists, 'it is at once evident that all those terms are borrowed from the vocabulary of *human system behaviour*. [They are] terms reserved for precisely the kind of complex group dynamics that cannot be pieced together by sheer summation of componental contributions'. Therefore, the argument that genes ' "determine" the systematic wholeness of the organism while at the same time being driven to "invoking" the analogy with human behaviour is logically a circular argument that we can readily dismiss from serious scientific consideration'.[139]

In addition, Weiss considers that the speculation about gene monopoly in organization 'also meets with *factual* contradiction': the speculation invests genes with 'animistic powers' if we grant them the faculty of spontaneous action.[140]

These observations show how Weiss differs fundamentally from his fellow biologist Dawkins for whom living structures *are* machines. Machines are constructed by people who impose an order on the parts which themselves do not possess the faculty to organize themselves. But in living organisms, this faculty must be assumed to exist in the cells as a hierarchical order.

The difference between the machine and a plant, an animal or a human body has been clarified further by J H Woodger by focusing on the inanimate parts on the one hand and on the live parts on the other. They are characterized by their respective relationships. In the case of the machine, these are called *external*, which means that the property of a part does not differ whether it is in the machine or is removed from it. Therefore, a faulty machine part is replaced by one taken from the store-room and no adjustment is required. But in a living being, there is an *internal* relationship, the properties of the parts being fundamentally different when they are within the organic hierarchy and when they are outside it.[141] Both Weiss and Woodger postulate a hierarchical order in organic nature, a teleology, but they do not agree with Dawkins's teleological machine-like investment of the constituents of the living whole. Weiss's reference to 'human system behaviour' refers to the fact that purposefulness is a human monopoly (if we exclude a theological interpretation). But although we do not assume that nature has a purpose when organizing itself, we cannot help explaining the parts of, say, a human body as serving a purpose – for instance, the heart to pump the blood into the arteries, or the lungs to safeguard the supply of oxygen to all cells and to eliminate carbon dioxide.

The microscopic constituents of the cell are intelligible also only if we make allowance for the function of the cell nucleus as answering the needs of the cell. An understanding of bodily wholeness as distinct from machine wholeness has crucial consequences when it is applied to the treatment of living organisms on the one hand and of machines on the other. If human organisms are treated as machines by medical science, interference in the functions of their parts by specific treatments follows. If wholeness is the relevant principle, treatments consist of an attempt to allow this intrinsic vital principle to assert itself by providing conditions under which it can operate. This means that there is trust in the healing power, the integrative force. Any attempt to interfere with the mechanisms is avoided as much as possible.

Such an approach characterizes a school of healing called Natural Therapy. It trains practitioners and it publishes literature in which the holistic-biological principle is expressed. Natural Therapy has two aspects. The first is concerned with the wholeness of the environment in relation to the whole of individual human health; this is the ecological factor of Natural Therapy. The second aspect refers to people's lifestyles, the habits on which their health (wholeness) depends, to their physiological wholeness.

6

NATURAL THERAPY

─────────────── • ───────────────

ECOLOGICAL WHOLENESS

The hierarchical principle calls for a sustained balance of the constituents of the body and also for a preservation of the balance within the natural environment. But a man-made ecology has arisen as the result of the Industrial Revolution, and people 'must now develop new attitudes towards achieving a civilisation which balances the two ecologies, natural and manmade'.[142] Natural Therapists are critical of the imbalance of the composition of the air which we inhale and of the soil in which our food is grown.

AIR

Pollution from car exhausts plays a major role in damaging people's health. Lead, derived from petrol and from exhausts, is now recognized as a health hazard and at last efforts are being made to restrict this source of ill health; lead is particularly harmful to children as it affects their brains and restricts their mental development.[143] Carbon monoxide emitted from car exhausts is another pollutant. It reduces the oxygen-carrying ability of red blood cells and aggravates chronic respiratory and cardiac disorders in susceptible people:

> In London, peak values can reach more than seven times the World Health Organisation recommended levels for long periods.[144] More than half the people who live in the US are exposed to levels of ozone higher that the concentrations recommended by the Environmental Protection Agency. High concentrations of ozone in rural areas are harming crops and, in the San Bernadino National Forest in California, extra ozone is upsetting the natural ecosystem.[145]

Hydrocarbon emissions from vehicles are a major cause of lung cancer, especially in urban areas. This could account for some 3,000 extra deaths per annum in Britain. Diesel fuel is more likely to be harmful than any other fuel.[146]

SOIL

Pesticides and insecticides are used on the soil on a wide scale. They upset the natural balance of the earth and also contaminate the water. The soil is a living structure which harbours bacteria, fungi, algae, protozoa and other microscopic organisms. They convert dead organic matter into its constituents and recycle it so that it becomes available to sustain life again. Of particular importance are the algae which fix nitrogen from the atmosphere, thus promoting the yield of this vital substance. Algae also contribute to the wholeness of the soil by providing between one-quarter to one-third of the available nitrogen for crops.

Agro-industrial science depends on artificial chemical fertilizers which interfere with the life within the soil. Furthermore, industrial sludge, which contains toxic metals, especially lead, cadmium and arsenic, adds to the disorganization.

One chemical fertilizer, nitrate, which is used extensively in high-technology farming, is particularly dangerous. It enters drinking water and is stored in vegetables – for instance, spinach. Babies are especially sensitive to it. The harm arises when it is converted into nitrite which occurs under many conditions of plant cultivation, storage and methods of harvesting.

Natural Therapists advocate the use of compost, a natural fertilizer, consisting of a mixture of animal and vegetable residues and a base such as earth, wood ash, chalk, sea-sand or a combination of them. Water and air are also essential. In the compost heap intense fermentation sets in, causing a rise in temperature, and fungi and bacteria break down the material. This constitutes a holistic approach.

PHYSIOLOGICAL WHOLENESS

HABITS

Apart from the dangers to health from the pollution of the air and the destruction of life within the soil, people's lifestyles and habits are of fundamental importance to their physiological well-being. Their health is their own responsibility.

Food

Eating habits play a major part in people's health. The effects of diet on diseases can be gauged from a recent report by the US government's senior medical officer:

> 1,500,000 of the 2,000,000 Americans who died last year fell to diseases related to a poor diet – including heart disease, obesity and cancer. Over-consumption of foods high in fat was cited as the prime culprit.
>
> The 800-page report, *Nutrition and Health*, found that though hunger is still present in American society, over-eating has become a greater threat to health. The report found that a quarter of Americans are over-weight, and that the problem is worst among black women aged 45 and over, 60 per cent of whom are overweight. Apart from overeating, the report also stressed Americans consume too much salt, sugar and alcohol.[147]

An article in the *British Medical Journal* provides further startling information: most of the dietary customs implicated in increasing the risk of cancer, overnutrition, excess intake of fat and meat and deficit of fibre are characteristic of the so-called 'Western diet'. Over half the cancers of the breast (541,000 cases yearly), two-thirds of colorectal cancer (507,000), and three-quarters of prostate cancer (198,000) – tumours which have been linked to such diets – occur in the developed nations.

As yet, we do not know confidently how to prescribe a risk-reducing diet other than in the most general terms: eat less; increase fibre, fruit and vegetables, and reduce fat. We conservatively estimate that, with present knowledge, it would be possible to reduce the toll of cancers by one quarter, or 1.5 million cases a year.[148]

Smoking

In the case of diet the holistic aspect is obvious, as food affects our whole body. With smoking the same applies. Recent reports from Britain and America highlight the damage to people's whole health from smoking. An article published in *Doctor* magazine in 1991 gave the following facts:

The smoking epidemic continues unabated, causing three million deaths worldwide each year and in the UK the annual toll is 110,000–300 deaths every day. Smoking causes three out of ten heart attacks and the same proportion of deaths from cancer. Lung cancer – the most common, killing 35,000 patients every year – would be virtually eliminated if people did not smoke. Of 1,000 young people who take up the habit, one will be murdered, six will be killed on the road and 250 will die from smoking . . . the quarter of smokers who die from their addiction do so on an average 15 years prematurely . . . Smoking is the largest single preventable cause of mortality. It accounts for a third of all deaths in middle age (40 to 64 years) . . . Inhaling the smoke of others can also be lethal. In the UK, several hundred people die each year from lung cancer caused by others' smoke . . . Many children lose time from school because of respiratory tract infections precipitated by their parents' habit . . . The problem of teenage smoking is massive. One-fifth of 15-year-old boys and one quarter of girls of the same age smoke. . . . And the incidence of smoking among young girls is increasing.[149]

In a more recent report, the figure of yearly deaths from smoking worldwide is some 3 million, expected to rise to 10 million a year in 30 to 40 years. A particularly large number of smoking-relating deaths occurs in underdeveloped countries.[150]

The American report gives details of the organs affected by smoking. Of all cancers in the United States, 30 per cent could be prevented if cigarette smoking were eliminated. Organs in direct contact with smoke – the oral cavity, oesophagus, lungs and bronchus – are at the greatest risk of malignancy among smokers.

As many as 90% of these cancers are attributable to smoking. Organs and tissues distant from smoke are also at some risk. Among smokers, rates of cancer of the cervix, pancreas, bladder, kidney, stomach, and hematopoietic tissues are increased 50% to 200% over rates in nonsmokers.[151]

Apart from causing cancers, smoking seriously damages blood vessels and the heart. In the lungs it causes bronchitis and emphysema; it is responsible for gastric and duodenal ulcers, for foetal malformations, abortions, stillbirths and low birth weight; it depresses the immune system and decreases fertility.[152] Smoking also increases the risk of occupational allergy.[153]

ALCOHOL

Alcohol dependence was listed as a mental illness in the first chapter. It was considered to be a symptom of the malaise prevalent in today's society. We shall now investigate distribution of the addiction amongst different sections of society and amongst different parts of the country. In addition, we shall estimate what harm alcohol does to the addict and to society as a whole, especially to people's bodies, minds and spirit. We shall discover under what circumstances people start to drink and how they can stop drinking.

Smoking often goes together with drinking.

> The social class of British drinking and smoking middle-aged men has shown a marked relation to their type of work: a manual worker is more likely to be a heavier smoker and heavier drinker than a person in a non-manual occupation. Places of residence also affect the tendency to smoking and drinking. An investigation showed that there were 'pronounced differences between the 24 towns [which were investigated] in the prevalence of moderated to heavy drinking and smoking, as well as what appeared to be a north-west to south-east downward gradient.'

Thus, the place where people live makes the difference in these habits.

There are different reasons why people drink. Some use alcohol for its tranquillizing effects, while others enjoy alcohol with their meals; for some people, alcohol serves as an important ingredient of social interaction and contact. These reasons differ from town to town and from region to region.[154]

This information demonstrates the complexity of the problem and the need to take into account all the reasons for drinking when therapists try to help people to break their habit. Apart from the reasons already mentioned, alcoholics often use drink to overcome agoraphobia and social phobia,[155] or to cope with their underlying state of depression. In such cases, confrontation of the particular emotional problem is required.

Whatever a person's reason for drinking may be, alcoholism is a terrible affliction. There are about 1.4 million heavy drinkers in England and Wales.[156] According to a leading article in the *British Medical Journal*,

> about 4% of the population in England and Wales and 10% of that in Scotland are problem drinkers – that is their drinking harms their health, occupation, or domestic or social life. Three quarters of problem drinkers are in employment, and about 5% of men and 1% of women of working age have some sort of drink problem. Alcohol related to sickness and absenteeism may cost industry £641m annually, and accidents and poor performance related to alcohol may cost £1.5 billion.[157]

Alcohol is also related as a major factor to suicides as well as to crime, as one study in England showed that '40% of the inmates of prisons surveyed had serious drink problems – this rose to 60% among petty recidivist offenders'. There is a further relationship to violence in the home and in particular to child abuse.[158]

As with cigarettes, alcohol affects the whole personality, but because the brain is involved, personality changes are far more serious than is the case with smoking. 'Alcohol abuse may produce pathology in almost any system.'[159] The liver is severely damaged by alcohol, but the stomach, the heart, the blood vessels, the kidneys and the lungs also suffer, as well as the muscles. Alcoholism may 'at least in part, have a genetic basis'.[160]

The chance of recovery has been investigated. As people take to drink for many different reasons, the statistics can give only an overall picture. Some combine leading stable lives with continual drinking, others become abstinent. Many move into and out of problem drinking.

There is also a physiological factor in those who stop drinking. It is concerned with the bodily withdrawal symptoms which occur when a drinker stops drinking. The temptation is to relieve these symptoms by starting to drink again. Those who are less dependent on drink may be less prone to 'reinstate the vicious circle than those who are severely dependent'. One study states that:

> Fresh hope and new self-esteem were important elements in the recovery of the men. Stability in a job and in marriage are important in the prediction of keeping sober. Some clinics have reported that 20–40% of their patients had done well, but there is evidence that people recover without attending for therapy. The use of Alcoholics Anonymous has been helpful to many.[161]

By adopting the wrong habits, millions die or suffer from illnesses, and their deaths and suffering could be prevented by a healthy lifestyle. People have been given the information by doctors and the media about correct eating habits and about the dangers of smoking and excessive drinking. The question is whether their consciences recognize them as false people by abusing their health. If that recognition is apparent, an appeal to change their attitude is indicated. It is still necessary to assess the strength of their motivation and the degree of their freedom to make a change. The people who use food, smoking and alcohol to allay their anxieties, those whose social milieu expects them to follow unhealthy examples, the many who feel driven to neglect their health because they are insecure without the aid of props, they all need treatment of their whole personalities and not just factual scientific information.

Cola, Tea and Coffee

The holistic approach of Natural Therapy includes a warning against the stimulation by tea and coffee. Although these agents are less harmful than cigarettes and alcohol, medical science has confirmed that they interfere with health if they are taken in excess, as is done by many people.

'A heavy user may be defined as one who takes more than 5 cups of coffee (100–150mg caffeine per cup) and 12 cups of tea (40mg caffeine per cup) per day'.[162] There are individual variations in the effects of these stimulants and how they affect the same individual at different times of the day. Some people are allergic to even small amounts. Those who become dependent on these beverages suffer from withdrawal symptoms when they go without their favourite cups. They experience headaches, irritability and the jitters. These symptoms are 'cured' by taking more caffeine poison, but they recur the following day. People who take high quantities of caffeine suffer from anxiety, depression, panic attacks, high blood pressure and even heart failure with palpitations. Their sleep is disturbed, they cannot concentrate on their work and may show abnormal behaviour.[163] Because tea contains tannin, it can interfere with the absorption of iron from food and can thus contribute to anaemia.[164] 'A daily intake of six or more cups of boiled coffee increases the serum cholesterol concentration in healthy subjects'.[165]

Breast-fed babies suffer from their mother's caffeine intake.[166] Cola, a favourite children's drink, contains 10–15mg of caffeine in 100ml. Pregnant women who take more than 150mg of caffeine per day are substantially more likely than others to have late spontaneous abortions.[167]

Natural Therapists advocate herb teas, dandelion coffee or other cereal coffee substitutes.

Unnecessary Medication

The habit of taking drugs that are not essential to combat an illness or to bring relief from pain which cannot be obtained in any natural way constitutes an unnecessary interference with the integrative processes within the body. Drugs are often used to relieve the results of wrong living. For instance, indigestion, in most cases, does not call for some mixture or tablets but for some regulation of the person's diet; laxatives are taken by people who could achieve normal bowel movements by taking more roughage in their food. Slimming tablets which frequently have serious side-effects do not solve the problem of adiposity. Sleeping tablets, which never produce natural sleep and often lead to hangovers, drowsiness and reduced performance at work, are misused on an enormous scale. They even lose their effect on people's sleep. Those who are kept awake by worries must seek a solution for their problems rather than blotting out their anxieties by taking a pill.

A drug may interfere with nature's healing process. Such is the case when patients reduce a fever which is not caused by a dangerous infection. As Elisha Atkins, the editor of an American medical journal has admitted, fever may be beneficial in a healing process.[168]

Many people develop a dependency on drugs. One author reported that 'four-fifths of the adults had taken or used some medicine in the two weeks before they were interviewed . . . Self-prescribed medicines outnumbered prescribed ones by two to one'. Two-fifths of the people interviewed had taken a medicine ten or more times during the day. But 'any drug that has been taken for longer than two years [unless strictly indicated] has a large symbolic component on which patients may be psychologically dependent'. Thus, people depend on the symbolic functions of prescribed drugs.[169]

The writer of a leading article in the journal *GP* has endorsed the view on unnecessary medication held by Natural Therapists. He traced this habit to 'the childish dependence of so many patients on the magical (or even mystical) effects of drugs'. People wrongly believe that by prescribing medicines doctors can solve

> any and every medical problem, restore diseased organs to perfect function and reverse the progress of old age or death itself. In fact, no drug can replace nature completely, and the childish reliance of the average patient on the drugs prescribed by his doctor may do harm in that drugs are relied on to do what the patient himself should do naturally. Good health depends fundamentally on healthy living . . . no drug, however wonderful, can replace the lack of simple fundamentals of healthy living, such as plenty of outdoor exercise, fresh air and sunshine, fresh wholesome food, sensible clothing, regular habits and moderation in all things.[170]

PRINCIPLES OF NATURAL THERAPY

These last observations, written for the journal *GP*, encompass the holistic natural therapy principle: that people's health depends on the way in which they conduct their lives, and that their health is *their* responsibility and primarily not that of their doctors. Their bodies work as a whole which means that all the individual parts and their functions are integrated within the whole organism, and damage to one part affects all the others and an improvement in one benefits the rest.

This holistic approach differs fundamentally from the approach of medical science which is analytical and classifies people as bearers of diseases which are treated by specific means – by drugs, surgery, radiation.

While Natural Therapy stresses the general principles of healthy living, it also pays attention to how individual people respond to food, exercise, sunshine and, moreover, to their attitudes towards their lifestyles. This matter is concerned not only with people's bodily constitution but also with their spiritual awareness of their true selves and how they exercise their personal freedom in satisfying the demands of their conscience. Limitations of that freedom were admitted in the first part of this book and are of great importance in this second part, which is concerned with bodily wholeness.

Food is obviously of fundamental importance. Fresh wholesome food is accepted as a necessity. But, as we have discussed already, food technology and agricultural technology destroy the wholeness of life within the soil and of the products which are grown in the soil. Thus, Natural Therapists reject the results of applied science and they differ from medical scientists in two important further respects. For them, the body is not a machine that requires food as its fuel. They disagree, therefore, with the science of dietetics which was found to have been derived from the concept of the body as a machine (*see* page 88). This view can be refuted by the fact that calorific requirements for human beings cannot be calculated accurately as fuel requirements can be determined for, say, motor cars. For instance, a person of a certain height and a certain age might retain his or her weight while resting in bed with an intake of 2,200 calories, while another person of the same height might need only 1,800 calories. Emotional factors also make a difference. The way in which the body deals with food is not machine-like: after the nutrients have been broken down in the intestinal canal, they enter the bloodstream, and the cells throughout the body select material from this source and return some of their own constituents into the blood. There is a constant process of rebuilding, which is utterly unlike what happens in a machine; it is a living process.

The second difference between the scientific and the Natural Therapeutic dietetic approaches consists of the classification according to the disease in the former but a general holistic approach, combined with personal considerations, in the latter. For example, the diet which scientific medicine recommends for the prevention of heart disease – namely, to reduce fat, and to eat plenty of fresh fruit and vegetables and fibre – is for the Natural Therapist the right diet for *all* people who wish to keep well. Natural Therapists also consider the needs of vegetarians or vegans (those who avoid not only meat and fish, but also dairy produce). As a rule, apart from raw salads and fresh fruit, protein is provided by yoghurt, soya products, a few eggs a week and meat and fish if people desire it, but fat meat is not recommended. Margarine made of plant oil or butter supply fat, and wholemeal bread, crispbread, oats, unpolished rice and potatoes supply carbohydrates. Vitamins and mineral salts are contained in these items in sufficient quantities.

The health of the bowel is safeguarded by such food. Attention is paid to the micro-organisms within the bowel – the 'bowel microflora' – the composition of which varies according to the food digested and which fulfils important functions for people's health.

Correct breathing is encouraged, special attention being paid to abdominal breathing which is concerned with the movements of the diaphragm, which is often neglected.

The skin is not ignored. Its health makes an important contribution to a healthy lifestyle. Its responses to sun, heat and cold are considered in every case.

Exercises, which are highly regarded by the leader writer in the journal *GP*, are graded according to people's strength and play a major part. So does attention to correct posture and the various systems of relaxation.

APPLICATIONS OF NATURAL THERAPY

The ideas put forward by Natural Therapy are sound common sense and do not run counter to the ideas held by many medical scientists. But the situation is different when the ideas are applied to the treatment of sick people. Then the fundamental difference between the two schools becomes evident, as does Natural Therapy's contribution to the prevention and treatment of sickness.

Whereas medical science looks upon patients as objects, to be treated according to the prevalent theory, whether by drugs or operation or any other method, Natural Therapy looks upon them as people who are responsible for their health. Although the Natural Therapist has to make suggestions regarding patients' personal lifestyles, it is up to them to change their way of living after they have realized that their illness is the result of faulty habits or that their state of ill-health demands a modification of their habits.

While scientific treatment is for a particular disease, natural treatment is for the whole person who, if health is to be restored, responds to the natural methods from a spiritual and biological point of view.

The therapist's responsibility is to assess the type of change which can be expected to bring about health, which means gauging correctly how drastic the treatment has to be. As the body is considered as a whole, *all* its functions are targets for the response in every case in contrast to the scientific approach which is targeted on the organ or any other part which has been diagnosed as the seat of the disease.

Diet

Food is of primary importance and here the natural way reveals its superiority over the scientific way. It avoids the faulty image of the body as a machine which, as we have discussed, considers food to be merely a fuel. A sick animal refuses its food and many sick people, especially during some acute illness, get better quickly if they take only water or fruit juices.

Such a fast can be a profound spiritual experience, during which people can take stock of their whole lives. It affects many organs, there is a loss of weight which improves the actions of the heart and lungs and lowers blood pressure. Bad breath and a coated tongue are interpreted as signs of the elimination of toxins. Regeneration of the tissues throughout the body takes place, a power which diminishes with advancing age.

Fasting is beneficial in acute and chronic diseases. A nasal cold, an attack of tonsillitis or bronchitis respond well to a fast, which also benefits sufferers from such chronic conditions as rheumatoid arthritis[171] and bronchial asthma. In very young and very old people and in sufferers from debilitating diseases such as cancer or diseases of the nervous system, a response cannot be expected.

A less drastic dietetic holistic stimulus is a regime of raw fruit; the next addition may be salads, then cooked vegetables, potato, unpolished rice, then wholemeal bread or crispbread, to be followed by milk products, eggs and finally a full diet.

Attention to the Bowel

The bowel responds to a change of food. A lacto-vegetarian diet has beneficial effects on the bowel flora.[172] The use of antibiotics, on the other hand, interferes with the normal pattern of the micro-organisms.

Natural Therapists avoid laxatives. Normal evacuations are facilitated by eating food that contains roughage such as wholemeal bread, salads, cooked vegetables, and cereals to which bran can be added. The bowel function is related to the whole body as, from its lumen, food is absorbed and any disturbance of such absorption affects other organs, including the blood, the heart and the way in which nutritive material is used to built up living matter. There is also a deep psychological significance: people feel emotionally involved in the action of their bowel. Many expect a 'clearing out' every day and do not realize that it is perfectly normal to have regular evacuations every second day. Not only are bowel functions experienced emotionally, emotions such as fear increase bowel activity and can cause diarrhoea. Emotional tension can cause abdominal cramps, which are constriction of the intestines. Some Natural Therapists use colonic irrigation and claim that harmful stool particles are removed in that way.

ATTENTION TO THE SKIN

The skin plays a vital part in the natural treatment of the whole person. Through it, people express their emotions; it blanches in cases of terror, it blushes in embarrassment, perspiration reveals fear or excitement, and any blemishes make young people in particular feel ugly, whereas a good skin is a sign of beauty. The skin is richly supplied with nerves and blood vessels which connect with those in other parts of the body. Elimination of toxins takes place through the sweat glands.

Perspiration is encouraged through the application of heat – for instance, in the sauna which can benefit many people, especially those suffering from rheumatism, although it is not recommended for elderly patients, or for those suffering from diabetes, heart trouble or high blood pressure. Local applications of heat relieve pain in the underlying muscles, but also in the inner organs such as the bowels and the heart.

The application of a cold compress is used to elicit a feeling of warmth, which means stimulation of the blood supply and sweat glands. The temperature and size of a cold compress allow the stimulus to be graded.

Different types of patients respond differently to such treatment, which has to be adjusted to a person's whole constitution.

Exposure to sunlight must be graded according to the skin's capacity to develop pigment. Reflections from the ground and from the sea intensify the effect of the sun on the skin. At high altitudes the power of the sun is increased and if the ground is covered with snow, the reflection is intensified. Patients can tolerate sun treatment more easily when they are moving than when they are resting. Sunlight stimulates the blood vessels of the skin and its glands and enables the body to produce vitamin D. Patients suffering from acne vulgaris and psoriasis benefit from exposure to sunlight. A recent increase in cases of malignant melanoma, the most dangerous skin tumour, has been attributed to injudicious exposure to the sun.

POSTURE

Correct posture is of fundamental importance. It consists of the correct relationship of the vertebrae and the head, as illustrated in figure 8.

When a person stands in a slumped position, the curves of the spine are exaggerated, the pelvis is tilted forwards and the abdomen sags. The lower back is too hollow, which gives rise to strain and fatigue. When the position is too braced, tension occurs in the muscles of the shoulder girdle restricting rib movement and consequently interfering with breathing. Breathing is restricted further when the stomach is held in. There is tension in the buttocks and the thighs, down to the feet. These faults are avoided when a person stands in the correct position (see figure 9).

As in standing, slumping must be avoided when sitting. The spine should be straight without being stretched, the shoulders should be neither braced nor drooping, making breathing effortless. The feet should be on the floor, slightly apart, so that there is no tension in the thighs, calves or buttocks. The hands should rest on the thighs (see figure 10).

Correct alignment while standing and sitting should be maintained when walking. The head, neck muscles and spine should be correctly balanced while the eyes look straight ahead.[173]

Attention to posture is not only important to prevent and correct bodily ailments, it is also important for people's psyche. A slumped position means a drop in a person's ability to cope with life; an exaggerated braced position indicates mental as well as physical tension. Becoming aware of the significance of correct posture and adopting the right stance, will help people to deal with their emotional problems.

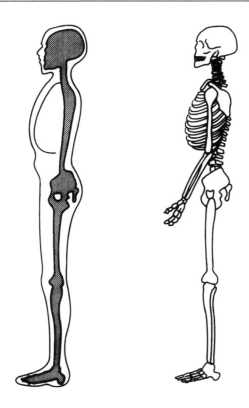

Figure 8 *Correct posture, showing the perfect alignment of the body*

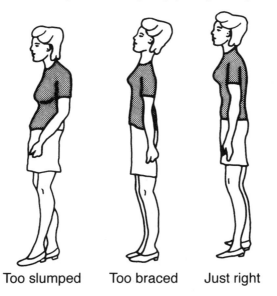

Too slumped   Too braced   Just right

Figure 9 *Examples of incorrect and correct standing postures*

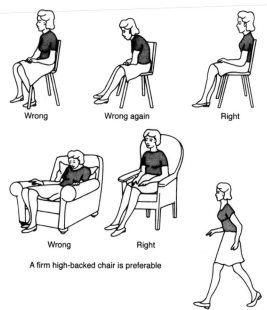

Figure 10   *Incorrect and correct postures for sitting in a chair and when walking*

EXERCISE AND RELAXATION

The scientific conception of the body as a machine fails when it is applied to physical exercise, for the outstanding feature is the need for self-regulation and adjustment throughout the body and the role of the mind: motivation and the determination to persist are essential. In Natural Therapy the holistic view of the personality is accepted. It is not only applied, for instance, to the rehabilitation of patients who have suffered a heart attack (which is also the practice of doctors, who are trained in scientific medicine) but exercise, graded to meet individual cases, is an integral part of any treatment.

As relaxation must be combined with exercise, those systems which involve body and mind are of special interest.

Tai chi is a fitness programme that began 2,500 years ago. It increases mental and physical energy through systematic stress reduction. It teaches a number of basic stances and individual movements which involve the whole body in graceful, flowing activity which tones up the muscles and increases flexibility.

An allied system is kung fu, meaning 'what to do'. It is of the same age as tai chi. It increases awareness and is a guide to fitness by developing agility and co-ordination, mainly through stretching the muscles.

Yoga is another gift from the East. It releases the life force that is within the body. It strengthens the body, gives it flexibility and elasticity and increases energy, while at the same time having a profound beneficial effect on the mind. The yoga teacher pays great attention to breathing. This exercise starts with exhalation, a complete emptying of the lungs. Then people inhale slowly, expanding first their abdomen and then their chests. Then the air is exhaled slowly. This complete breath provides for a good supply of oxygen to the whole body and thus people gain alertness, overcome fatigue and increase vitality.

A system which is related to yoga called 'autogenic training' was designed many years ago by a German doctor, J H Schultz. Patients sit in a comfortable position or lie down with their eyes closed; they are given suggestions by the therapist and these are turned into auto-suggestions. The keynote is calmness. It is related to muscle-tone, peripheral blood circulation, heart beat, breathing and the nerve supply within the abdomen. As a contrast to the warmth of the body, coolness of the forehead is suggested. Not only does this training improve bodily functions, it also improves memory and sleep, and it helps people to recover from the effects of strain. After the various stages of this psychosomatic training have been mastered, pupils are introduced to a higher stage when they imagine a colour which to them expresses harmony and they then reach a state of contemplation.[174]

There is a widespread use of relaxation treatments. Transcendental meditation, yoga and the other systems are very popular. Autogenic training is widely practised in Germany by general practitioners. But such methods are not part of a scientific medical curriculum and they do not figure in medical textbooks, for they do not follow from the mechanistic conception which classifies patients according to their diseases. But scientific medicine cannot be ignored because Natural Therapy has its limitations.

LIMITATIONS OF NATURAL THERAPY

Although nature's integrative healing power is a guide for Natural Therapists and is trusted to respond to the modifications of the patient's lifestyle, this trust is not absolute. For nature is not always holistic and there may not be a beneficial response to the holistic stimulus.

Therefore the therapist has to *assess* in every case of illness what response can be expected and, if a favourable reaction has not taken place or is not likely to occur, all the methods of scientific medicine have to be employed. For instance, an attack of diarrhoea may be interpreted as a healing effort on the part of the patient's body to eliminate some toxic material, in which case no effort would be made to stop the symptom. But if the patient was losing too much fluid and valuable tissue salts in his stools, the therapist must replace such losses and, if a virulent infection has overwhelmed the body's defences or is likely to do so, an antibiotic may have to be given to assist in the struggle for recovery.

The uncertainty of a response to natural treatment, compared with the certainty of a response to such scientific treatment as the injection of insulin in a diabetic, highlights the limitation of Natural Therapy. This is to be expected, as we do not know the living organism as a whole and can only influence the hierarchical power by altering conditions under which it operates, whereas medical scientists do know the workings of individual bodily processes such as the sugar metabolism of diabetic patients. Natural Therapy relies on the purposeful, healing tendency within the body, but, as we learn from Kant, purpose is an idea which is applied to life by analogy with our own purposeful activities, and life remains a mystery, to be respected and cherished.

Although the limitations of Natural Therapy cannot be overcome in principle, certain methods which are allies to this form of treatment and which do not interfere with it can be added to its practice, thus extending its therapeutic potentials. These methods also accept the notion of the wholeness of the body, but they are *applied* to the patients and thus lack the appeal to their freedom which confers on Natural Therapy the status of a treatment for the whole person, including his or her spirit.

ALLIES TO NATURAL THERAPY

HOMOEOPATHY

Homoeopathic medicines, which come from the animal, vegetable or mineral kingdoms are for whole persons, for their bodies and their minds. The treatment may be for a skin eruption or an ulcer in the stomach, but it is not just for such objective signs of illness. The remedy covers the subjective side of a problem – the itching of a rash, its relief from being covered or uncovered, the type of stomach pain, its dependence on food and on the position of the body. The mental side of the personality is taken into account: a person's irritability, depression, a longing for certain foods, a dislike of others. People's constitutions are considered: different remedies are given to those who are cold and those who need cool air, and to those who are intellectually alert and those whose intelligence is impaired. The remedy covers patients' physico-mental make-up.

Homoeopathic remedies work on the principle that like should be cured by like (*homoeo* means like, *pathy* means suffering). Sick people are cured by medicines which are known to produce symptoms and signs like those of the patients if they are taken by healthy volunteers.

Not only are remedies prescribed for different types of people, they are also prescribed to prevent diseases. Here is a bridge to the principle of immunization, which is accepted by medical science. Moreover, homoeopathic prescriptions are designed to help patients in their recovery from the after-effects of illnesses such as influenza and pneumonia when the body has overcome the acute infection.

Although the remedy may be given in material doses, it is often diluted (in a special way) to the extent that no molecule of the original substance – for instance, sulphur – is left. The efficacy of such 'high potencies' has been proved by using controls in the case of hay fever.[175] In order to explain a non-material effect, quantum theory can be cited which employs a wave and not a particle model. Homoeopathically prepared solutions may [thus] be considered to have far-reaching effects. The remedy may produce a 'field effect' over the entire organism. This remarkable holistic phenomenon is significant, as 'a small fluctuation such as a microdose can effect a movement toward healing'. The whole explanation is not in terms of 19th century scientific ideas which are still 'most prevalent in modern biology and conventional medicine', but in terms of 20th century physical science.[176]

Natural Therapy and homoeopathy share the concept of a patient's vital force which is stimulated by the treatments. Both let the effects of such stimulation take their course before the treatments are changed. Both consider aggravations as healing efforts which are not to be stopped. Information about patients' sensitivities to heat and cold elicited by the homoeopath, is of value to the Natural Therapist in the choice of cold or warm applications to the skin.[177]

Because of their common ground, homoeopaths should accept Natural Therapy as providing the basis for the efficacy of their treatment. In doing so, they would follow Samuel Hahnemann, the founder of their school. He insisted that if the homoeopathic treatment is unsuccessful, the cause must be sought in 'some circumstance in the mode of life or the surroundings of the patient which must be changed before a permanent cure can be made'.[178] He stressed further the importance of 'exercise in the fresh air, simple, suitable and unspiced food and drink and surroundings uplifting the spirit'.[179]

Homoeopaths should face their patients with the true-self ethic. In the search for the remedy, emotional states such as fear, irritability, lack of confidence and indecision are elicited and patients are made aware of such feelings. As these are relieved by the treatment, people should be encouraged to confront their situations and to meet the challenges of their lives.[180,181,182]

Even with all these extensions, homoeopathy must admit limitations in its curative powers. Another ally to Natural Therapy, acupuncture, offers additional help for patients.

ACUPUNCTURE

As a form of traditional Chinese medicine, acupuncture considers the human body as a whole. Health is said to depend on a balance between two forces – yin and yang. If either preponderates, disease results. A third force, chi, sustains all kinds of movement and change; it also protects against harmful influences. It flows in channels, called meridians. Acupuncture points lie on these medians and, by needling them, the acupuncturist restores the disturbed balance.

The holistic conception is evident, as a disease imbalance is said to be caused also by the environment which includes wind, cold, heat and dampness. Further factors are found in people's diets, in their physical and sexual activity, the way in which they live and in their emotions.

Western scientific medicine does not accept the holistic metaphysical explanation of traditional Chinese medicine. Its own narrower interpretation is in terms of the nervous system; its holistic character consists of its distribution throughout the whole body and in its relationship to the mind. In fact, current neurological knowledge is not sufficient to account for all the phenomena, which are observed by acupuncturists, but a basic understanding is available: the central part – the brain and the spinal cord – are not only related to all the peripheral parts, but its own parts are interconnected also. Thus, a spasm in a neck muscle which gives rise to a nerve impulse in the upper part of the spinal cord can travel downwards and cause a pain in one arm, which can also be elicited by a spasm in a muscle of one leg, the impulse this time travelling upwards. Thus, pain may be referred from one part of the body to another and an acupuncture needle, inserted into the point from which the pain has been referred, into the trigger point, abolishes the pain of which the patient complains.

In addition, nerve impulses travel horizontally and are related to the different segments of the spinal column. Needles, inserted into this path are also beneficial. Furthermore, the actual site of the disturbance may be treated successfully with a needle or with firm pressure.

Needling releases opium-like substances within the body. These affect the nervous system, including parts of the brain from where powerful hormones are secreted which influence many parts of the body. There may also be an effect on the immune system.[183]

MASSAGE

Apart from applying firm pressure to trigger points, massage represents another ally to Natural Therapy, aiding the whole body in the process of recovery. There are different techniques: light and firm stroking, kneading and hacking movements. The aim is to encourage the flow of blood and lymph; to reduce muscular tension and to provide a general calming and soothing effect. Local sprains and congestions are relieved by firm pressure. Massage of the whole body and individual parts, limbs, abdomen and chest can be carried out by patients themselves, or, when the back is included, by professional people. This treatment is often combined with active and passive movements of the various joints.

OSTEOPATHY

Another form of mechanical treatment, which is allied to Natural Therapy and frequently combined with it, is osteopathy. Although the technique is applied to individual parts of the body, the aim is to serve the whole. Any disturbance in the structure of the body which is apt to interfere with normal reflex activity and the flow of blood and lymph is called an osteopathic lesion which may also result in a biochemical fault and may disturb the function of the nerves. By correcting such lesions, the osteopath restores the disturbed equilibrium, whether the trouble origi-nated in the spine or whether it arose within the body and affected the vertebral column secondarily.

The manipulations not only aid lymphatic drainage locally, they benefit the internal organs, such as the heart, the stomach, the kidneys and the bladder. Allergic conditions are said to respond by reducing hypersensi-tivity, which is evident, for instance, in bronchial asthma.

CHIROPRACTIC

Chiropractors differ from osteopaths by employing a different technique when carrying out manipulations. They are mainly concerned with correcting spinal joint dysfunction, but they also treat joints throughout the body. Like all other forms of natural medicine, the treatment relies on the body's inherent healing properties.

Osteopaths and chiropractors have to face the limitations of their techniques. Joints may be too deformed to allow successful manipulations and violent movements of the vertebrae may endanger the integrity of the spinal cord. But even if communication with the whole body has been established, and if the other methods of natural medicine have been employed, people may still require the help of scientific medicine.[184]

In this chapter we tried to discover how, in an unnatural scientific – technological world, the wholeness of health could be saved. The discussion started with considering the wholeness which is naturally obtained in the environment in which lives exist. The damaging effects of various substances in the air we breathe and in the soil in which our food is grown call for efforts by Natural Therapists to redress the balance. Apart from unholistic and unwholsome soil cultivation, man's own additional unbalanced diet as a cause of serious diseases was documented and such harmful habits as smoking and excessive consumption of alcohol provide further strength to the cause of Natural Therapy. While its limitations are recognized and it is admitted that drugs might be required in cases of severe and serious illness, a vast amount of unnecessary medication is condemned. In the clinical application of the principles of Natural Therapy, it is stressed that all the functions of the body are considered, which represents a crucial difference from scientific medicine which divides the body into parts and diagnoses diseases accordingly. We find that Natural Therapists increase the range of their treatments by adding those which also consider the whole person, although they are administered to the patients and are therefore not an aspect of Natural Therapy which calls for the observance of a healthy lifestyle. The methods that were discussed were homoeopathy, acupuncture, massage, osteopathy and chiropractic, all of which are highly popular with patients.

7

EXAMPLES OF NATURAL
TREATMENTS FOR THE
WHOLE PERSON

———————————————— • ————————————————

After the theory and practice of natural therapies has been discussed, this chapter applies these methods to patients. They had all been diagnosed as sufferers of some specific condition. This diagnostic approach will be shown to require a non-scientific holistic correction and it will become clear how a biological holism that deals only with the wholeness of the body must be related to the higher spiritual holism in order to do justice to the whole person.

EXAMPLE 1: MUSICIANS' PAINFUL TENSIONS

Many stringed instrument players, percussionists and pianists are greatly troubled by painful tensions in their arms, wrists and fingers. They are usually treated by scientific medicine:

> rest is the cornerstone of the treatment; this is best achieved by lightly bandaging the hand with a crepe bandage, which serves mainly to remind the patient not to use it. Inactivity should be enforced until spontaneous pain or pain with unavoidable use of the hand, such as personal washing, has subsided. Patients need to be warned that the pain in the hands or forearms may worsen for up to three weeks after they start a radical regimen of rest or after palpation of the tender sites.

Pain in the shoulder is treated by the use of ultrasound to a back muscle (trapezius) and a neck muscle (sternomastoid).[185]

But, as another writer has remarked, symptoms, relieved by rest, return when playing is resumed and the treatment 'remains controversial'.[186] Some members of the International Society for the Study of Tension in Performance share this view.

Therapists who treat the whole person, which includes the whole body, and who prefer to use natural means, interpret tension and pain in the muscles of the arms, wrists and hands as the result of trigger-spot activities in the muscles elsewhere. By systematically testing, such points may be discovered in the muscles of the shoulders, arm-pit, shoulder-blades, neck, back and as far away from the parts of which the musician complains as the buttocks, thighs and even in the muscles located within the pelvis. These areas of tenderness are abolished by the insertion of needles and by deep massage which is painful at first but becomes painless as the muscle returns to normality. There is immediate relief of tension and pain in the muscles used in playing. The treatment has to be repeated several times, but the musicians themselves are instructed in how to find all the areas of muscular tension in their own bodies and to eliminate them by deep massage. After such self-massage, they are encouraged to carry out a certain yoga exercise which is designed to loosen the whole of the vertebral column from where the nerves that supply the muscles originate. The slogan they have to follow is: 'tune your body as well as your instrument before you start to play'.

In order to avoid tension, it may be necessary to correct a faulty posture and a faulty instrumental technique. One contributor to the problem of musicians' painful tension maintains that

> it is unfortunate that the right kind of expert help is not yet readily available. Not all teachers seem to know enough about the correct use of the body to diagnose the various kinds of misuse that cause pain, and doctors do not know enough about instrument techniques to suggest what a player may be doing wrong. The skills needed to play most instruments are extremely refined and delicate, seldom demanding strenuous efforts (such as an athlete may have to make); when the posture is good and the body well balanced and free of unnecessary tensions, no physical harm should result, no matter how long the playing.[187]

Treatment of the whole person includes the mind and spirit where tensions may originate apart from the body. It is essential to enquire into emotional situations which may give rise to serious conflicts. For instance, one girl, a gifted violinist, was much distressed because she was on bad terms with her parents. Each time she spoke to her therapist about her home life she became aware not only of her anger and resentment, but also of the tension in her muscles, the result of her emotional state. She gradually gained an understanding of the total family situation and thus the freedom to play without restriction.

Finally, tension arises from the players' careers, from the doubts about their talents, from their fear of competition and from the tasks of mastering the art, and from doing justice to the grandeur of the compositions. Players require understanding and encouragement from their therapists to overcome these sources of tension.[188]

EXAMPLE 2: SUFFERING OF AN ASTHMATIC

Autogenic training was earlier described as an important method for patients' integration of their whole personality. The following is an account of an asthmatic woman's achievement by this method:

> Yes, I have a breathing problem. It is no exaggeration to say that my breathing has been bad for many years. I have been classed as a 'chronic asthmatic' recently, in addition, as a sufferer from emphysema, which means that parts of my lungs have lost their elasticity, so that the air sacs can no longer hold the necessary supply of oxygen. Asthma is a constriction of the bronchial tubes which makes exhaling especially difficult, at times almost impossible. Thus asthmatics suffer from fear and panic which makes great problems for these people who are rather sensitive.
>
> Asthma is a complex complaint, it has many contributing factors: allergy, infection, hormones and most important emotions. Apart from taking many drugs I have been helped by homoeopathic medicines, by acupuncture and by pressure applied to sensitive areas of my body, but autogenic training has been of the greatest assistance, for I am now aware of the emotions which cause the wheeze and I am more able to control my breathing so that I can alleviate the attacks and calm those which are more severe. Autogenic training is a form of self-suggestion, leading to intense relaxation.
>
> It took me six weeks to learn the different stages and three months to master the technique. I had been my own worst enemy, as I was fighting against the treatment at the beginning, as it struck me as bizarre, weird or even alien. How could I achieve the various steps, leading to total awareness, while I was only aware of my inability to breathe. These are the stages: Stage 1: 'I'm calm.' – 'You must be joking, I'm jumpy as a flea on a hot plate.' Stage 2: 'I'm heavy.' – 'Not at 7.5 stone.' Stage 3: 'I'm warm.' – 'Try and convince yourself of warmth while you are shivering because of lack of oxygen in your blood.' Stage 4: 'My heart is beating calmly.' – 'Oh yea, you should feel it!' Stage 5: 'My breathing is easier.' – 'As my sons would say: "this is the ultimate sick joke" when I am wheezing like an accordion.' Stage 6: 'The pit of my stomach is warm.' Stage 7: 'My forehead is cool – not easy to feel.'
>
> These were my reactions at the beginning of the training, but I had not realized that my muscles were completely relaxed and, to my great surprise, I did begin to notice various things: I did feel warm, my heart was beating more slowly.
>
> I can now, at any given moment and in any place, whether alone or surrounded by people, go into the autogenic training which takes two to four

minutes. If I have been exhausted (which is frequently the case as I am still a workaholic), I go into a very deep sleep for an hour at the end of the training exercises, and this is extremely helpful after a severe attack. I wake up refreshed and ready to cope with my enemy – myself. The gradual rise of calmness with the improvement of breathing needs to be experienced to be fully appreciated. Now that I am no longer a novice, the autogenic training runs by itself. For as I concentrate and say 'I'm calm', heaviness, slower heart beats, calmer breathing etc follow on without my actually having to say the words to myself. The muscular relief is fantastic, as asthmatics suffer from aching muscles which are overworked when struggling, grasping for more air. I'm in control, I'm calm, heavy, warm, my heart is beating slowly, my breathing is getting easier and the pit of my stomach is warm (and all the digestive juices make enough noise to prove it); my forehead is cool and I look inwards and see my favourite colour lilac. I am aware, I am!

I have to remind myself that I am getting older, but now there are things I can do which I could not do as a youngster, not even eighteen months ago. This week I walked my dog for thirty-five minutes in the morning, my worst time for breathing. I can sit now in the dentist's chair and suffer the horror of cold cement and warm wax for fitting dentures, keeping my mouth closed and still breathing. I can face any obstacles. Autogenic training has made me totally aware of myself as a whole. Not that I am completely changed. I still flap, get over-emotional, feel things too deeply, get more disturbed by my environment than I should. I am still too hard on myself, push myself too far and neglect my body, but autogenic training and reveries have taught me to be totally aware of the whole me.

EXAMPLE 3: SKIN IRRITATION AND DEPRESSION

Although the effects of emotional troubles on the skin are well known, there is still a tendency for patients to be treated by separate departments of medicine.

The following case illustrates how a whole person was suffering from an emotional-spiritual crisis which manifested itself on the skin and how the equilibrium was restored through holistic treatment. The patient, a woman of 46 and a trained nurse, was referred because she had suffered from rashes which had not responded to antibiotics and also from emotional stresses which had not been relieved by an anti-depressant drug. The rash was mostly on her legs which had been scratched and there were a number of boils.

Her history was as follows: her childhood had been unhappy; her parents divorced when she was a baby, her mother remarried and her stepfather assaulted her sexually. Her own marriage had been unhappy because of her husband's adultery. She got a divorce. Then she met a man whom she loved and who, she thought, loved her. This relationship came to an end when she discovered that he had concealed the fact that he was married. Her mother was the person who had been close to her, but she had died of lung cancer three months before the consultation.

The patient had one daughter and two sons, one of whom, a drug addict, was in trouble with the law. Her main professional occupation was mostly administrative and not fulfilling, but her evening work as a district nurse was creative.

She smoked twenty cigarettes a day, nibbled a lot of sweets throughout the day and the rest of her diet was as follows: for breakfast she had two cups of coffee with lumps of sugar; for lunch, white and brown cheese rolls; and for her supper she ate an egg, fruit, vegetables and fish.

Her periods had stopped two months before.

The mother had suffered from the same kind of rash as the patient, and the mother's rash had appeared at the sudden death of one of her sons and was still present at the time of her death. The patient had nursed her mother until she died.

Holistic assessment

Here was a woman who felt that her whole life was in tatters. She felt angry about her fate, especially about her mother's recent death and about the deception of the man whom she had loved. She was eating large amounts of carbohydrates to gain some comfort. She also used cigarettes to relieve her emotional tension.

Her rash had an emotional basis: it served as an identification with her late mother and the scratching marks were the result of her anger and despair. The excess of carbohydrates in her diet had led to an excess of stored carbohydrate in her skin which had promoted the development of septic lesions.[189]

Treatment

Clearly, the aim was to help the patient to discover the way to be a whole person again. This meant that she had to regain her faith in God which had been shattered after her mother's death, in people which had been shaken by her lover's deception and ultimately in herself as a true person who could cope with her life without bitterness and resentment. Her therapist revealed this task to her.

It was not a matter of expressing her anger, but of making the patient aware of that anger which had led to self-destructive moves towards her body, causing her to smoke, to over-eat, especially starchy foods, and to scratch, and towards her spirit, causing her loss of faith. Through the encounter with her therapist she succeeded in realizing her freedom.

She accepted the following diet: breakfast was to be muesli, yoghurt and herb tea; lunch to be fresh fruit, cottage cheese and wholemeal crispbread; and dinner, cooked vegetables, potatoes baked in their skins, cheese or a soya dish, fish a few times a week and fresh fruit. She thus reduced her intake of carbohydrates and was urged to stop smoking.

She agreed to take a cold shower morning and night to revitalize her skin, which would also help other parts of her body.

The second consultation was two weeks later. She had followed the diet and had reduced her cigarettes to five per day. She had stopped scratching, her skin was dry, there were no more boils and the scratch marks were healing. She felt well in herself and had been able to pray again, the first time since her mother's death. She had realized how angry she had felt, but she had overcome her anger.

On the occasion of her third and last consultation she was less composed. Her son, the drug addict, had been in trouble with the police after he had stolen a prescription and had procured massive doses of valium and analgesics. She had attended the Court hearing. Her other children had rejected their brother. The question was whether she should do the same and not allow him to stay in her house. She felt strong enough to have him at her home, provided he attended a psychiatrist.

Another boil had formed on one of her legs, but this temporary set-back was not the result of a rise of sugar in her tissues, as a blood-sugar test gave normal results. It was the result of the shock, caused by her son, and she recovered from this upset.

Two months later the patient reported on the telephone that she had come to terms with her life. She had not developed any more boils. For the last month she had stopped the cold showers, but she still applied cold water to her legs. She had modified her diet, had salads on most days and avoided an excess of carbohydrates. After several relapses, she had stopped smoking.

Additional treatments

1 Homoeopathic remedies: staphysagria (stavesacre) in the 200. potency as a help to cope with the insults she had suffered and with her

anger; sulphur, silica and carbo vegetabilis in the 6. potency, and belladonna and hepar sulphuris (Hahnemann's calcium sulphide) in the 30. potency to assist the healing of her skin; and mezereum (spurge olive) in the 6. potency to relieve the itching.

2   Acupuncture, applied to her neck to loosen muscular and, indirectly, emotional tension.

The examples of natural treatments of a whole person demonstrate the value of acupuncture and massage in cases of the muscular aches of musicians, of autogenic training for a sufferer from bronchial asthma and of diet, homoeopathy and acupuncture for a woman troubled by skin irritation. In all these cases the complaint and the treatment were related to their whole personalities: in the musicians to emotional tensions in their personal lives and in their artistic involvement; in the asthmatic woman her whole outlook was changed; and in the last case anger and resentment were faced and overcome which led to the recovery of spiritual and bodily wholeness.

It may be argued correctly that any improvement in a bodily condition is bound to affect the whole person, as all people are units of body, mind and spirit, but the spirit is the predominant element.

These patients, having suffered from bodily complaints – muscular tension, bronchial constriction and skin irritation – did not recover as the result of the application of mechanistic medical science. They gained spiritual health, exercising the freedom of their true selves. They joined those who, we found, had responded to true-self psychotherapy: the woman who, with the aid of her poetic awareness, discovered the road to self-assertion; the patient who had been thrown into depression by her experience of her son's schizophrenic illness, but who gained her true self partly through artistic expression and partly through overcoming wrong attitudes and wrong dependency; and the third who, in using her strength to draw self-portraits, recovered her true self. They joined the fourth who liberated herself from her mother's hatred of men, and the fifth whose dream helped her to become aware of her femininity. Furthermore, they joined the Cornelius Ryans, the France Pastorellis and the René Maugrases who, we saw, achieved spiritual victories in the face of crippling bodily suffering. They all won entry to the realm of the spirit which was earlier characterized as the realm where people progress to their potentially true selves, subject to the authority of their conscience, where they exercise their personal freedom, where conscience is an autonomous force, not derived from social influence. Here courageous, responsible decisions are made and artistic creativity, manifest by the application of true-self therapy, flourishes. Imagination, expressed in reveries, plays a further part in the struggle for spiritual wholeness by enabling one woman, for instance, to find out about her weaknesses and strengths so that she could face her fears, tears and horror and then find hope.

Hope is shared by all who trust the voice of their conscience and who gain health from spiritual and biological holism. Innumerable doctors and their helpers tacitly accept the true-self ethic. Apart from treating their patients' bodily and mental diseases on mechanistic principles, they support their spiritual striving for a true self in the face of pain and distress. This orientation is evident in counsellors who try to enable people to face and cope with fatal conditions such as AIDS. Many sufferers need to find hope and a balance between being realistic about their illnesses and enduring the restrictions that are due to physical and mental deterioration. Other counsellors' spiritual work is concerned with strengthening those who have been bereaved or who have endured ghastly experiences such as torture.

While there is no animosity against such holistic spiritual practices, some medical scientists have shown intense hostility towards holistic practices. They treat illnesses on mechanistic lines and claim to have a monopoly on their treatments. In the following chapter, the strength of the alternative holistic movement is assessed and the claim that all treatment must conform to the criteria of scientific medicine, which means that holistic medicine is denied a place of its own, is rejected.

The complexity of technological medical science stands in sharp contrast to the simplicity of biological holism, evident in Natural Therapy, although its practice demands the frequently difficult exercise of spiritual freedom, evident in a reform of people's life styles.

The position of holistic medicine in the whole field of healing is then defined.

8

HOLISTIC AND SCIENTIFIC MEDICINE

———————————— • ————————————

DISENCHANTMENT AND THE ALTERNATIVE

'The Road to Disenchantment' was chosen by the *British Medical Journal* as a title when it reported on the television series, *Doctors to Be*. The series follows medical students to their time of qualification and their activities as junior hospital doctors. *Doctors to Be* presents cogent arguments for change. The disenchantment was expressed by one participant: 'It could have been such a wonderful thing to be a doctor – but it's not. It's just a disaster.' The reporter concludes as 'the strongest message' from the programmes that 'a medical education does not prepare you for becoming a doctor'. 'The most moving moment' is recorded when a house officer awaits the arrival of an elderly patient late at night. He admits: 'I've felt . . . you know, I just wish the patient would die before getting here. Because then I won't have to go through the rigmarole of doing an ECG [electrocardiogram], taking blood . . .' The conclusion is: 'He's not alone.'[190]

'Rigmarole' refers to medical technology which threatens to over-whelm doctors. It is evident in all medical specialities which, in the words of another critic, imposes on medical students an 'excessive burden of factual information'.[191] Many members of the public share doctors' disenchantment and turn to alternative forms of medical practice.

Holistic medicine, also called alternative or complementary medicine, is popular in America and in Europe. In Belgium

> about one in four [citizens] visit a complementary practitioner, in Denmark [the] ratio of alternative practitioners to family doctors [is] 1 to 1.6, in Finland more than a quarter of the adult population have used some form of complementary medicine, in France about one in four general practitioners

care for patients using complementary treatments, in The Netherlands complementary medicines are flourishing in response to public demand, about one in eight of the British population use complementary medicines . . . Some patients probably use both forms of health care.[192]

In Great Britain the number of lay practitioners in 1981 was 27,800, compared with 29,800 general practitioners in 1982. A survey undertaken among young Scottish doctors who had just completed their medical training revealed that out of 100 doctors, 86 declared that they had a positive attitude to alternative medicine, 18 of them were using at least one alternative method themselves, and as many as 70 expressed their wish to train in one or more areas of complementary health care; 31 had referred patients for such treatments and 12 of these had made referrals to non-medically qualified practitioners. Thus, alternative methods of treatment are being used to complement conventional medicine and 'expansion in their use appears imminent'.[193]

In Germany there is a growing demand for complementary medicines. They are used by about two-thirds of the population and over half of the people are convinced of their benefits. Over a third of general practitioners and hospital specialists frequently prescribe alternative remedies, 'and only 8% would refuse a patient's request to do so'.

These facts were revealed by a survey initiated by the Federal Ministry for Research and Technology in Bonn which found that 'the most widely available complementary therapies are, in order: phytotherapy (herbal treatment), homoeopathy, anthroposophical medicine, physiotherapy, and acupuncture'. The biological holistic claim is stressed: complementary medicine aims at 'an active participation of the organism in self-healing and regeneration'. This is contrasted with 'artificial, non-natural treatments', used by 'conventional medicine' which 'are claimed to assign a purely passive role to the organism, aiming to eliminate pathological changes'.

The problem of research was investigated and although there had been research into 'the five most available forms of therapy', it was considered 'flawed by poor quality of designs of clinical trials and incomplete presentation in papers'.

It is important that 'a large proportion of complementary medicine' was thought to be 'accessible for scientific evaluation justifying further research and sponsorship by the Ministry for Research and Technology in Bonn'.[194] In Britain there are plans for this type of research.[195]

The survey by the German Federal Ministry for Research and Technology calls for an evaluation of the scope of such assessment with regard to alternative medicines. One question is: can a holistic biological approach be subjected to a mechanistic scientific investigation; can a patient's holistic integrative unspecific power be tested by the adoption of the mechanistic principle, tied to the concept of disease specificity? If it is only a question whether patients improve under the holistic treatment, then their illnesses will also show an improvement.

The success in a controlled trial of fasting and one-year vegetarian diet quoted earlier proved that patients suffering from rheumatoid arthritis benefit from Natural Therapy dietetics which ignores scientific dietetics. For the medical scientists the success is explained in terms of specific mechanistic medicine: it is the result of removing food allergy or food intolerance in the patients or to 'an extensive change of the profile of the fatty acids' in the blood.[196] For the Natural Therapist such changes are a *holistic* response to the *holistic* stimulus of a drastic change in diet. Fasting, like any change in a patient's lifestyle, is not a treatment for a particular disease, but for a person whose illness is judged to need such a change to which a favourable response from the whole personality can be expected.

The fact that electroacupuncture, another form of alternative medicine, is effective in relieving the symptoms of fibrositis, which include pains in the muscles and constitutional symptoms such as fatigue, disturbed sleep, giddiness and abdominal discomfort,[197] is explained by the holistic practitioner as the result of the normalization of an imbalance of vital forces or of the activities within the body's nervous system.

The medical scientist, on the other hand, explains the benefits in terms of a change in neurohumeral mechanisms and of a release of pain-relieving substances within the body. The fact that beneficial changes only occured when needles were inserted into 'true' acupuncture points and not into 'false' random ones is accepted as proof of a positive control test.[198]

Anthroposophical medicine, popular in Germany and practised also in other countries, is based on Rudolf Steiner's occult science. According to Steiner, the human physical body is related to the dead world of the mineral kingdom, the etheric body is shared with the plants and the astral body with the animals. He assumed that the astral body develops into spiritual activity.[199] One anthroposophical remedy is mistletoe or iscador. It is used for the treatment of cancer, acting by 'increasing resistance to the proliferative tendency of the cancer cells'.[200] Although no control trials of iscador have been published, it is likely that these would be positive, as a large number of publications have shown that iscador inhibits cancerous growths. Such therapeutic results would in no way confirm

Steiner's view of the human organism and in particular his view of the cell which turns into a cancerous cell. According to Steiner, this change can be explained as 'man is a whole, related to the cosmos and has always to fight against the obstinacy of the cells'.[201]

The spirit in Steiner's occult science of anthropology occupies the leading role in his writing but a separate wholeness of the body is not recognized. For instance, the activity of bodily nerves is not considered to be an anatomical–physiological activity but a spiritual one. Emotional life, which includes the interplay of love and hate, is interpreted as having its foundation in rhythmical breathing. Other functions, such as intestinal movements, kidney activity, sleeping and waking are all synthesized in a united spiritual wholeness. A spiritual world is postulated into which man's soul and spirit enter after death. The whole edifice of this occult science is explained as knowledge and not as faith.

Medical scientists cannot accept holistic treatments within their own system which involves the use of specific interference within the organism, often with dangerous side-effects. This is in contrast to the harmless but beneficial effects of holistic treatments which inspire holistic practitioners and their followers. The results obtained from such treatments are interpreted by medical scientists in terms of their own mechanistic approach.

Such an interpretation was not found possible in the case of the successful control experiment which was carried out by homoeopaths who treated hay fever with the 30. dilution of pollen (already quoted). This went beyond the stage when molecules of the pollen were present in the preparation (the last molecules are eliminated in the 12. centesimal dilution, called 'potency', and dilutions of the 200, 1,000, 10,000 and 100,000 potency are being used). As the particle model of physics is not applicable, the other model which physicists recognize as accounting for physical reality, the wave model, has been cited in the form of 'fluctuations', caused by the homoeopathic remedy within the organisms (*see* page 109).

This explanation, however, runs into insuperable difficulties, as it assumes that each homoeopathic remedy causes its own fluctuations and each dilution results in a more or less intense one. The control test proved that the treatment was effective, but physical science, fully accepted by medical scientists, cannot account for the beneficial effect. Sir James Jeans, a celebrated physicist, provides the answer to the dilemma: he chooses the wave picture of a free electron and asks:

what happens to the waves when there is no human consciousness to represent [them]? For we must suppose that electrons were in existence while there was still no human consciousness to observe them, and that there are free electrons in Sirius where there are no physicists to observe them. The simple but surprising answer would seem to be that when there is no human knowledge there are no waves; we must always remember that the waves are not part of nature, but of our efforts to understand nature.[202]

What applies to the wave picture also applies to the particle picture. This does not mean that the material universe with its biological aspect is unreal. It means that 'our restricted minds' can make the universe 'intelligible' only by using 'mechanical terms'.[203] Reality, apart from the operations of the human mind, is unknowable.

We saw that Erwin Straus drew the same conclusion when he refuted cerebral determinism of the mind, pointing out that scientific knowledge does not represent objective brain material but the products of the scientist's mind which create concepts such as synapses in cells (see page 25). The conclusion follows from Kant's theory of knowledge, according to which the world (reality), apart from the knowing mind, the architect of knowledge, using as its tools its cognitive conceptual faculties, is unknowable.

Not only have medical scientists to accept that they have no knowledge of what really is happening in nature, they also have to accept that their method of testing the efficacy of a treatment, described as derived from a machine-like conception of the body, is not valid for testing the efficacy of holistic treatments, as these do not deal with homogenous groups of disease sufferers but with individual, unique people.

The musicians who were relieved of their painful incapacitating tensions could not be matched with a comparable number of patients suffering from the same symptoms. The violinist who found the strength to resolve the conflict with her parents was helped individually and not as a member of a homogeneous group.

Each of the other players had to overcome his or her tensions by a personal understanding of his or her body in relation to personal posture (with its personal emotional relevance), of his or her whole life as a musician, and then had to apply that knowledge to help overcome their disability.

The patient who gained relief from her asthma through autogenic training cannot reasonably be likened to other asthmatics who may not have the same strength and imaginative power as she had – qualities which elude objective assessment.

The nurse's skin irritation could not be compared with similar sufferers who scratch their skins, as their irritation may not be due to the same over-indulgence in carbohydrates as the result of emotional tension, nor would other patients be expected to share the same spiritual conflict.

All these patients manifested their spiritual wholeness, their ethical freedom by the way in which they faced their illness, guided by the demands of their conscience in accordance with the true-self ethic which is valid for all people, although individually they accept the ethical challenge.

With regard to biological holism, allowance was made for limitations in the treatments based on it. But such reservation is not accepted by dogmatic metaphysical schools – for example by the Chinese version of yin and yang and by the occult science of anthroposophical medicine. This does not mean, however, that a critical holistic practitioner cannot use acupuncture and remedies such as iscador, allowing for the limitations of such measures.

Such a balanced view is foreign to scientific medicine. In their arrogance and ignorance of the limitations of the applications of its mental constructs, medical scientists not only demand proof of any treatment by successful control design, they restrict the use of acupuncture to pain relief, which they consider to be suitable for 'a small proportion of patients'. They deny the effects of acupuncture, osteopathic treatment and chiro-practic for the whole organism. As for homoeopathy, only the practitio-ner's and patient's faith, and not the chosen remedy, is said to account for good results.[204]

Two doctors of philosophy writing in the influential American *New England Journal of Medicine* find less academic words in their attack which singles out the holistic aspect of alternative medicine. They ridicule

> this rhetoric claim that manipulating a part of the body somehow restores an inarticulated 'balance' or 'harmony' to the whole. At the base of the litany that each person must be treated as unique, that every part of the body is interdependent on every other part, and that body and mind are inseparable is the claim that holistic practitioners are absolved from demonstrating causal relations between their treatments and alleged therapeutic gains. They are under no obligation, they believe, to reconcile their claims about therapy with what is known about causal pathways of the body.

Such practitioners are said to hold an 'antiscientific' point of view,

> however much holistic therapists may parade what they take to be the trappings of science. Consequently, they make every effort to disparage

rational assessments of their practices. A magical view of nature and mind and a mystical conception of knowledge are opposed not just to scientific conclusions but to scientific reasoning.

The same authors find an explanation for the fact that holistic medicine is widespread and enduring: 'there is no reason to take its claims seriously; superstition, self-deception, stupidity, and fraud are ubiquitous and always have been'.[205]

HOLISM FIRST, SCIENCE SECOND

In its defence holistic medicine has to provide evidence that the millions of people who receive alternative health treatment are not being exploited and tricked by ignorant and ruthless practitioners, many of whom are doctors, and that people are justified in denying conventional medicine the claim of possessing an exclusive approach to health and disease. In the conduct of this defence, the arguments, which have been discussed in support of holistic medicine throughout this thesis, are summarized and their need for acceptance is demonstrated. As conventional medicine has concentrated its attack on the holistic treatment of the body, biological holism is defended first. In this respect opponents of complementary medicine reveal their ignorance of the theory of organic nature.

Conventional medical treatment of the body, we saw, is restricted to the idea that the body is a faulty machine which, to quote the words of the writers in the *New England Journal of Medicine*, leads to knowledge of 'the causal pathways in the body'[206] which accounts for the knowledge of specific mechanisms and its applications, but which cannot explain or act upon the hierarchical character of life.

The writers of the same journal reveal their ignorance when they ridicule the rhetorical claim that manipulating a part of the body somehow restores an inarticulated ' "balance" or "harmony" to the whole', or when they mock 'the litany that each person must be treated as unique, that every part of the body is interdependent on every other part'.[207]

There has been a change of heart in some quarters of the medical establishment. Doctors could not deny that patients had improved under 'alternative' treatments and some who speak for the medical fraternity have graciously agreed to accept alternative medicine, but on condition that each treatment has passed the same test for efficacy that scientific therapies have to pass. This condition is unacceptable. It denies the justification of holism in medicine. Even if such tests are successful, as the case of the homoeopathic treatment of hay fever which involves high dilutions of pollen, or the case of an anthroposophic treatment for cancer with iscador, or of fibromyalgia with acupuncture, the results are evaluated only from the narrow mechanistic scientific point of view. Such testing cannot reveal the effects of these holistic treatments on the *whole* person. Also, as has been shown, the controlled experiment, the hallmark of scientific testing, cannot be applied to those treatments in which a unique individual response occurs, such as the cases of the handicapped musicians and the woman who suffered from skin irritation and depression.

Some representatives of the scientific world support the application of holistic biology. Bernard Dixon, as Editor of *New Scientist*, has been critical of the view that progress in medicine must be sought by discovering specific remedies for diseases in order to find the 'magic bullet' to hit the illness. As an alternative to 'the seductions of high technology medicine' he has strongly advocated 'the alternative approach that seeks to maintain health rather than to treat disease'. He has claimed that only 'in a little over 10 per cent of the cases medical intervention succeeds dramatically, by the administration of antibiotics, by surgical manoeuvres, or other specific measures. . . . What is drastically amiss is the notion that there is a specific drug to cure everything – a belief that has retarded our thinking about alternative approaches to health and disease'.[208]

Confirmation of the value of holistic medicine on treatment of the body also comes from an illustrious member of the medical profession, Thomas McKeown, who wrote:

> medical science and services are misdirected, and society's investment in health is not well used, because they rest on an erroneous assumption about the basis of human health. It is assumed that the body can be regarded as a machine whose protection from disease and its effects depends primarily on internal intervention. The approach has led to indifference to the external influences and personal behaviour which are the predominant determinants of health.

He lists 'over-eating, under-exercising, smoking, and the like' as factors that will have to be changed if there is to be progress in health. What is required is a modification of lifestyles.[209]

While Dixon makes allowance for specific treatments with antibiotics and surgery, his emphasis is on the unspecific approach which is the holistic one, aimed at bodily health. While he recommends an acceptance of biological holism, he is also aware of the crucial role of the mind in such cases as smoking and faulty eating habits. He thus calls for educating people about their health.

McKeown goes further than Dixon. He touches medical science on a raw nerve when he asserts that the body is not a machine; therefore, conventional medicine, based on the mechanistic principle, is mistaken. He recognizes the size of the problem, of changing the direction of medical science: medicine 'will remain unchanged so long as the concept of disease is based on a physico-chemical model'.[210] He recommends that medical scientists should 'shift' laboratory research to epidemiology[211] – that is, disease should be studied as a mass phenomenon, and a whole group of people, a community, should be investigated.

The results of such research are now known. They were quoted with regard to the extent of mental disease, of drug addiction, of suicides, deliberate self-harm, AIDS, of disease due to smoking, to alcohol abuse and faulty nutrition. Social scientists provide further knowledge regarding why people destroy themselves: people in modern Western society have lost their bearings, their values, their innateness, their symbolic universe. Life is experienced as meaningless and science has no answer to offer. The medical student, fed with an ever-increasing amount of knowledge was quoted, saying: 'It could have been such a wonderful thing to be a doctor – but it's not. It's just a disaster' – a disaster for him and for his patients.

While Dixon and McKeown provide a welcome antidote to the arrogance of medical scientists, no modification of science can do justice to spiritual holism, on the acknowledgement of which humanity's future depends. By applying their only approach – which looks at the body and the mind in the same way that a motor mechanic looks at a car – the approach of mechanistic determinism – the scientist denies personal freedom and the ethic of the true self which are demanded by conscience, replacing it with a hedonistic ethic – Freud's pleasure principle. The frameworks of neurological, reflexological, libidinal and archetypal mechanisms and the teleological social interest were all found to be obstacles to a realization of the spiritual holistic ethic. As in the case of the application of biological holism also in spiritual holism, practitioners must not be dogmatic and must accept limitations in the use of the spiritual-libertarian approach. This fact was already stressed when it was conceded that sufferers from mental illness may not be free to realize their ethical freedom and may therefore require treatment as objects of organic psychiatry. However the vast numbers of anxious and desperate people, of drug addicts and the thousands who attempt suicide or injure themselves by taking overdoses of drugs can recover their lost true selves only by finding the strength to realize their spiritual wholeness. They have to replace their 'protean selves' by their true selves; and they have to cease being 'creatures of immediate appearances and sensations', dedicated to a 'sensate, direct life of experience' which deprives them of making long-term commitments.[212]

The validation of the true-self ethic is seen in the way that ordinary people cope with their lives, including how they deal with their illnesses and death. A form of true-self psychotherapy is outlined and illustrated by examples.

D E Roberts's interpretation of existentialism is accepted as a confirmation of spiritual holism and of the true-self psychotherapy. His protest against the validity of scientific truth as a means of grasping reality, constructed as a logical system, is joined by our protest against the scientific theories which make patients and others into libidinal or archetypal or reflexological objects, or into the results of a socio-economic nexus. Roberts's insight into the subjective truth of personal fears, hopes and other emotions is shared when patients' struggles for selfhood are followed. Finally, his emphasis on the tension between people's personal freedom and their involvement in a natural and social order is a reminder that they have to face and deal with such involvement (*see* page 84).

Although biological holism is treated as a distinct subject from spiritual holism, the spiritual dimension extends to the field of bodily health and ill-health. As the account of Natural Therapy shows, a lifestyle involves taking responsibility and thus the realization of personal spiritual freedom.

Medical science is accepted to treat those mental illnesses which deprive patients of their spiritual freedom and also to treat those whose bodies cannot be expected to respond to holistic natural stimuli. Thus, medical science complements holistic medicine and that is its limited use.

Scientific medical truth – the manifestation of a current theory which is replaced by another in due course, providing only temporary factual knowledge – will have to take second place in medicine, to be applied only when biological and spiritual holism cannot treat a case. Where healing is required, holism will be used first, while science will be second. In that way faith in the mystery of life and in the freedom of humanity will make selfhood meaningful.[213]

A holistic integration and an analysis of the parts of the body that function mechanistically are not the only considerations in a person's health. The relationship that exists between people requires further attention, not only from a collective but also from a personal point of view. The third part of this volume is devoted to this issue. The finite boundaries of an individual's world are to be transcended and the strange infinite world of the other is to be welcomed.

PART III

———————————— • ————————————

SELFHOOD IN INTERPERSONAL RELATIONS

9

THE SELF AND THE OTHER

In the preceding sections of the book the emphasis has been on the individual self and the ethical question has been whether people are judged by their conscience to have coped with their lives, including their conflicts, their illnesses and their death, as true selves. The adverse conditions of contemporary Western social life were accepted as hindrances to true selfhood. The true-self psychotherapy was illustrated by cases in which people had to liberate themselves from the harmful influence of certain members of their families. But the enemy was not always another person; often it was the person's own self-destructiveness which had to be recognized and overcome. The woman who gained her freedom by abandoning her rejection of her husband confirmed Karl Jaspers' view which is quoted, according to which the overcoming of the external force depends on interpreting it as an 'element of one's own existence', an internalization of her mother's hatred of men (*see* page 78).

This egocentric orientation of the true-self ethic is justified as the subject of the enquiry is personal health, which depends on the achievement of biological-spiritual wholeness, but it also depends on the relationship with fellow human beings, with the Other. We shall be guided in the interpretation of this relationship by the French philosopher Emmanuel Levinas who has clarified the experience of the meeting of the self and the Other.

Levinas poses the question: 'why does the Other concern me?' He explains that posing this question means that individuals are concerned primarily with their own selves. This premise is incorrect, however, for individuals are responsible for each other, otherwise 'there can be in the world no pity, compassion, pardon and proximity'. Thus, it is essential that the self puts itself 'in the place of the Other [and] to communicate is indeed to open oneself' which involves 'becoming a responsibility "for the Other".'[214]

According to one commentator, 'the Other faces me in the poverty and nakedness, and the majesty of his face. To recognize the alterity of the Other is not to grasp, to conceive it, but to answer to his solicitation', to his earnest seeking an answer from me, which is 'meaningful for him [and an] answer for my being'.[215]

This means that the Other is in a weak position, appealing for help from the strong self which has the responsibility to answer the appeal. But in the cases quoted earlier, the position of the self and the Other was the reverse: a strong Other ignored or overpowered a weak self which had to defend itself against the Other. Thus, the ethic operates in both cases, the self having to be true to itself and true to the Other.

Such a move goes beyond toleration which would mean that I can just bear the Other and his strange world, suppressing negative feelings. The strangeness may well provoke a negative response at first; we are so different, we may appear to be incompatible. I must reverse this negative judgement and Levinas shows the way: people are inclined to think in rigid, finite terms, in categories such as 'friendly' or 'unfriendly', 'intelligent' or 'stupid', 'reliable' or 'unreliable' and so forth. With such words they tend to sum up the Other and his entire personality.

In order to change this approach fundamentally, Levinas insist that when approaching the Other I have to welcome the expression on his face 'in which at each instant he overflows the idea [which] a thought [of one of the rigid categories] would carry away from it [the expression].' Instead of the finite idea I have of the Other, the overflow has resulted in the 'idea of infinity'. I now have a perspective which is prior to my way of summing up people. Instead there is an immediate experience which bears no intervention. 'The immediate is face to face.'[217]

Levinas calls the face-to-face situation 'an ultimate situation' which is not just momentary: 'Even when I shall have linked the Other to myself with the conjunction "and" [,] the Other continues to face me, to reveal himself in his face. Myself and the Other do not form a totality, we are not integrated as parts of a whole. If totality can not be constituted it is because Infinity does not permit itself to be integrated [and] it is not the insufficiency of the I that prevents totalization, but the Infinity of the Other' [and] the face-to-face relation is 'an irreducible relation'.[218]

The infinity of facial expressions reflects the infinity of the possibilities of the human personality, but the ethic of welcoming the Other and for making an allowance for his or her infinitude may make unattainable demands and should be interpreted as an aim which cannot always be achieved. This is because, in the human personality there is unfortunately not only potential infinitude, but also finitude which limits the scope of the personality.

When persons recognize their duty to do justice to the strange world of the Other, they have to call into question their spontaneity. This is required by the presence of the Other and this self-criticism is called ethics.[219] Individuals may be proud of their performances as a writer or sportsman, but their partner, the Other, cannot be expected to share their enthusiasm – hence their need to find a proper perspective of what is so precious to them and which has no place in the Other's world. All these considerations also apply to their partner, for whom they are the Other.

Levinas reminds his reader that it is language that 'offers things which are mine to the Other' and further that language 'presupposes interlocutors', people who can talk and want to talk. Of course language can also be misused, suppressing the Other. I can make him agree with me by the way in which I talk to him. But in any case, by addressing him, I call on him to reply.[220] According to Levinas, it is the relationship with the Other which is ethical[221] and, therefore, it is unethical if in one's choice of words and deeds one fails to reach the necessary standard.[221]

For Levinas, to live is to enjoy life. To despair of life makes sense only because originally life is happiness.[222] Enjoyment embraces all relations with things,[223] but 'in enjoyment I am absolutely for myself.' An 'egoist [is] without reference to the Other . . . not against the Others . . . but entirely deaf to the Others, outside of all communications'.[224]

The statement that I cannot share my enjoyment with an other may seem untrue, but it is right: my enjoyment of food, of my favourite tune or of the sunset is entirely 'egoistic' and I cannot expect my closest friend to share my enjoyment. If I express my disappointment that he is not with me in such moments, I spoil our relationship. In fact, 'enjoyment accomplishes separation',[225] forces upon me the fact that I am alone. Of course I enjoy my friend's company and he enjoys mine, but we each have our own private enjoyments. Also, I must not take my joy for granted, as 'joy remains a chance and a stroke of luck [and] the happiness of enjoyment . . . can be tarnished by the concern of the morrow',[226] when I am no longer lucky.

Aloneness is necessary, for 'the idea of infinity, revealed on the [Other's] face, does not only require a separate being; the light of the face is necessary for separation'.[227]

A very special relationship is formed between a man and a woman. Levinas interprets the I–Thou 'in which Buber sees the category of interhuman relationship as the relation with feminine alterity'. The relationship is not confined to words, but it is 'the source of gentleness in itself'. [228]

> Language does not belong among the relations that could appear through the structures of formal logic; it is contact across a distance, relation with the non-touchable, across a void. It takes place in the dimension of absolute desire by which the same is in relation with an other. The Other is neither initially nor ultimately what we grasp or what we thematize. 'Truth is in transcendence'. [229] . . . It is only in approaching the Other that I attend to myself.

In discourse, individuals expose themselves, their personal world to the Other's world, and the Other expects their response, which is their responsibility to provide. They must be attentive. [230]

Face to face, the ethical relation with the Other, introduces in individuals what was not in them before. Their minds have been transformed. They are now the target of the Other's appeal which calls them to be responsible for the Other. [231]

Love remains a relation with the Other that turns into need, but the Other retains his or her alterity – there is both need and desire. [232] Love aims at the Other, love is to fear for another. [233] This means that the Other serves the self, although the self is deeply concerned about the beloved. In sexuality, attention is no longer on the lover's face, but sensuous pleasure has taken over. This is different from friendship, but there is a condition: 'I love fully only if the Other loves me' [234] – both partners need mutual sensuous pleasure . . . Levinas goes further: 'to love is also to love oneself in love'. [235] The self that experiences the Other's love experiences itself as lovable. Thus, the strangeness of each Other's worlds is one of mutual enjoyment. All these assertions presuppose that the partners are not only engaged in sexual activity, but in love which involves bodily pleasure.

When sexual promiscuity with its risk of infection with AIDS and other sexually transmitted diseases was discussed, Erich Fromm's views were quoted (*see* page 18) which confirm Levinas's conviction that the desire for physical union must be inspired by spiritual love.

10

GUIDANCE FOR MARRIED AND UNMARRIED COUPLES

———————————— • ————————————

Relations between married and unmarried couples fail if their physical union is not inspired by spiritual love. Those who act as professional guides bear a heavy responsibility if they do not convey to those whom they counsel the ethical view of the self and the Other.

EXISTENTIAL COUNSELLING

Emmy van Deurzen-Smith, President of the Society for Existential Analysis in Britain and the author of a book on existential counselling, agrees with Levinas that people live in their own worlds. But for her, these worlds are defined as the natural, the public, the private and the ideal. This means that people are not granted an infinity and her definition of ethics varies fundamentally from Levinas's: conscience is said to be an obligation to make the best use of opportunities and, with the encouragement of a counsellor, people's aim is to 'expand their repertoire'.[236]

The application of this ethic is illustrated in the case of the marriage of Paul, who had a good job, and Miriam, a teacher, who was also earning a good salary. After they had overcome their sexual inhibitions, 'love-making had been wonderful' for the wife, but when she discovered that her husband could not father a child, she became bored with the incessant sex. The 'natural and the public domain' could no more provide satisfaction and Miriam now explored the 'ideal domain' which meant teaching abroad. However, Paul was not prepared to leave the country and thus their marriage came to an end.[237]

Paul's and Miriam's marriage and divorce is typical of millions of other failed marriages: each partner selfishly aims at looking after his or her own world and does not welcome the Other's world which is strange and does not provide the opportunity to expand their repertoire.

Their sexuality was devoid of spiritual love; neither her work as a teacher in England nor her husband's sterility were for Miriam challenges that she was prepared to meet. According to van Deurzen-Smith, 'living in accordance with one's inner sense of purpose provides motivation beyond the mere fulfilment of duty. It makes one feel truly and passionately alive and it makes life all the more worthwhile'.

In Miriam's case the inner sense of purpose called her to be adventurous and to teach in the Third World rather than fulfil her duty as a wife. She thus acted according to the duty of self-fulfilment rather than to the ethic of 'calling into question her spontaneity'. We must agree with van Deurzen-Smith that when people follow their ideals they must be willing 'to face up to human limitations'.[238]

We have also agreed that not only infinitude but also finitude exists in the human personality, and that people who take their marriage as a commitment ought to aim at welcoming and accepting their partners in their worlds. Without that aim, a marriage is liable to break down – the fate of one in three marriages in Britain now, with millions of children left as casualties.

Miriam had felt that the challenges as a teacher and as a wife in a childless marriage had not been 'great enough'.[239] Therefore she had tried to kill herself by cutting her wrists, acting the heroine.[240]

Miriam's counsellor 'was to help the client to trace back her original intention, her deepest sense of what it is important to achieve in life'.[241] By interpreting this most important achievement in egoistic terms, the counsellor is seriously mistaken. Miriam and others like her are not served well by this ethic, and her new 'ideal world' will not satisfy her in the long run.

SCIENTIFIC SYSTEMIC COUNSELLING

The majority of marriage counsellors are trained in a scientific approach, with different theoretical models acting as guidance. The common concept is that the marriage partners operate in a system which may be considered to be part of the wider family system, which includes parents and their children. The two partners have their individual subsystems and the problem is how to create 'a mutual and workable system', as we learn from a recent writer on the subject.[242]

The fundamental objection is that, as Levinas has insisted, 'the Other is neither initially nor ultimately what we grasp or what we thematize' and the Other's face 'overflows [with] the idea of a thought' (see page 136).

The relationship is ethical, concerned with the infinity and not with a reality that, in the words of David E Roberts quoted earlier, can be grasped primarily and exclusively by intellectual means (*see* page 82). We agreed with this author's 'emphatic denial of the assumption that construction of a logical system is the most adequate way to reach the truth' (*see* page 82). Our objection to the systemic use of science in the case of marriage counselling is strengthened by the insight we gained from the Oxford philosopher Collingwood – namely, that an abstract law 'ignores the omnipresent individuality of the real' (*see* page 83), the real person with infinite potentialities.

One system is based on the theory of psychoanalysis and especially on the variety that is concerned with object relations. The practice was criticized earlier as it reduces people to libidinal objects. This feature shows itself most clearly when it is applied to marriage partners.

The author of the book from which the creation of a workable marriage system was quoted reports how one counsellor interprets the idea of the self objects in psychoanalytic ways: 'each [partner] uses the other "to maintain", restore and consolidate the internal experience of the self'. We also hear that other followers of the psychoanalytic school 'explore the evolution of reciprocal agreements which couples make with one another'.[243] This sounds like a business arrangement whereby partners are primarily concerned with their own advantage. There is every chance that one or the other will complain about not having received a proportion to which he or she is entitled. In that case there would be no point in continuing with the unfavourable business.

In the scientific spirit counsellors ascertain the level of interaction between the partners and try to understand the rules on which they were operating.[244] All this spells inevitability and leaves no room for the freedom of new attitudes, which are taken up in accordance with one's conscience. It is the dead hand of science.

Counsellors have to confront marriage partners with facts which interfere with the marriage relationship. For instance, a husband may have to be faced with the evidence which he has tried to ignore – namely, that he is repeating his father's hurtful treatment of his mother in the way he treats his wife.

If the counsellor accepts and applies Levinas's ethic concerning human relations, the factual confrontation would be followed by the ethical one: the husband's conscience would be faced with his guilt and with his freedom to change his attitude towards his wife. This relational approach would be on the same lines as that used in individual true-self psychotherapy, illustrated by the comments from the patient who, with the therapist's help, corrected her mistaken view of conscience: she considered that 'the most helpful thing' in the treatment had been being asked 'the question "why?" and what things stood for'. After this factual confrontation, the patient could accept responsibility for her life, which meant that she was ready to confront her ethical duty towards herself (*see* page 73).

A case taken from Margaret Robinson's book on systemic counselling, illustrates how the ethical approach differs from the factual-scientific one. Anita, a London librarian in her early thirties, met John on her holiday in Australia, moved into his flat and became pregnant by him. He offered marriage, she panicked. Their son David was born. John was delighted. Anita found fault with John because of his drinking and because he spent time with people she considered to be a bad influence on him. John had a row with Anita's parents. The relationship broke up and solicitors took over, assisted by the counsellor.[245]

If Anita had been guided by a counsellor who follows Levinas's ethics, she would have been asked to face the factual challenges of a life in Australia with John whose habits were foreign to her. Her ethical duty would have been presented: to welcome John in his world as well as for the sake of their child, who would need a father's and a mother's love. The feelings of panic may have passed under such guidance and her life with John and their child may have been greeted as fulfilment.

John, on his part, may have found the strength to overcome his dependency on alcohol; he may have developed new friendships if he had been convinced of such needs. His offer to marry Anita and his love for David would have been interpreted as favourable signs for a future with Anita. In spite of their efforts, the marriage may still have ended in failure if they were unable to meet each other's needs without being untrue to themselves. But they would have grown in stature and would not have had to bear guilt towards each other and towards their child.

Marriages represent a special case of dyadic relations. Treatments of groups of different sizes will now be examined from the point of view of true selfhood which has been the ethical concern throughout our discussion.

11

GROUP PSYCHOTHERAPIES

•

TRUE-SELF GROUP TREATMENT

The same ethical principle of confrontation which is employed in individual true-self therapy, can be applied to groups. The atmosphere must be one of mutual support by members. As with individual treatment, discussion is helpful.

DISCUSSION

At the regular weekly meetings, the participants are asked to address themselves to one topic, relating the problems of their lives to it. The following is the record of a discussion entitled 'What are we afraid of?'

Ruth: 'I'm afraid to be like my mother.'
Susan: 'I'm afraid of not being good enough for my parents. I'm also afraid of my own ideas and thoughts, I might hurt other people.'
John: 'I'm frightened that I might become like my younger brother who is very disturbed. I can't face my fear.'
Therapist: 'But people have to face their fears, it is the aim of the treatment to give them courage to do so.'
Albert: 'I'm afraid that I'll follow my father who has opted out of responsibilities and has left the family.'
Charlotte: 'I am frightened of travelling or of going into a lift.'
Bernard: 'I've just started work as a messenger. Everybody is looking at me, I'm angry with the people, I'm scared of them, but also afraid I might hit them.'
Albert: 'I feel like Bernard.'
Esther: 'I'm alone in the world, my fear is that I might get ill and nobody would look after me.' Her fear was confirmed by Susan.
Susan: 'To be left without help is also one of my fears.'

Charlotte: 'And mine too.'

Pauline: 'Mine as well, especially as I don't think that my GP is interested in me. I have no friends and no relatives.'

Brian: 'It's heights, crowds, travelling in the underground that scare me.'

Leonard: 'I have had such fears, but I have been able to overcome them. I hope you will too.'

Evelyn: 'I'm afraid people will reject me, therefore I keep away from them. I know this is wrong, I feel confused and don't know what to do.'

This record of the discussion does not tell whether Evelyn found the strength to face her fears of rejection, or whether the other members overcame their fears and doubts. But they were all given an opportunity to confront their anxieties and one may assume that they felt encouraged to cope with them and were helped by the fact that they had shared their experiences with each other.

Apart from gaining insight into their own problems, they had gained insight into the way how others felt and how they felt about each other. They may also have recognized feelings they had for people who were not members of the group.

An outburst by a woman who attended a group meeting revealed her attitude towards men in general: 'I feel annoyed that the men are dominating the discussion.' This gave a chance to face her problems with men and to find out how she could stand up to them.

A woman who was suffering from long-standing depression, attended another meeting at which the question was: 'How can we overcome our resentment?'. The depressed patient identified herself with a teenage daughter against whom a fellow patient had expressed her resentment. She admitted later to the psychiatrist: 'My depression comes from submerging my identity, trying to think what my mother wants me to be.' She was helped further when another depressed patient, also a member of the group, started to cry. She told the psychiatrist after the meeting: 'I wanted to go to the crying patient and hold her hand, but I was not strong enough to cross the room'. By experiencing her own emotional responses, this patient put her discovery thus: 'I had not given up finding my true self. This awareness has encouraged me enormously and has given me hope.'

ART

As in individual therapy, so in a group setting, art can help patients to face their situation and to find their true selves. Patients are asked to paint whatever comes to their minds, such paintings often revealing their emotional conflicts. All the paintings, when finished, are displayed in front of the group and the members are invited to make comments on their own and other members' paintings. Figure 11 is an example. Members of the group offered the following comments on this picture: 1 Naïve; 2 Avoiding the common path; and 3 Picking fruit.

The patient, a middle-aged single woman, responded to these interpretations:

> 1 and 2 are no doubt true. I feel that I'm too innocent to have lived at all yet, and I'm afraid of the common path of life. As for 3, I just don't know exactly what this indicates. Does it mean that I'm now able to reap some reward from my treatment, from my sustained effort to get well? The harvest is not yet very satisfactory. There are still lots of ways in which I'm bound, tied and unable to move, yet I long to be free.

The members of the group were able to identify with the patient and they were moved by her picture and by their own comments to consider their own true paths.

Figure 11 *In group therapy, patients freely express their thoughts and emotions through the medium of art for discussion*

Reading suitable plays aloud permits members of the group to identify with the characters and then to discover the significance the play has for their lives. It is another way of liberating the true self. An example is Ibsen's *A Doll's House*, which illustrates the effect of a possessive husband on his 'doll wife'. Many modern plays provide opportunities for identification with characters who suffer from marital or other common problems.

Apart from help gained from discussions, from works of art and from spontaneous drawings, dream interpretation, carried out in a group setting, is therapeutic.

DREAM INTERPRETATION

A group of eight to ten patients met once a week and on each occasion the therapist asked one of the participants to describe a dream. The others were invited to relate the message of the particular dream to their own lives. The following are examples for which suitable headings have been chosen:

Interpretation 1: Parental Influence

Pauline related the following dream: 'I'm walking home from a party, an unknown man joins me and protects me with his umbrella against pouring rain. I let him take me to a bus stop which is not my usual stop. I later lose him and I see my father and my aunt watching me.' When questioned, Pauline explained that her father had been very possessive and had always warned her against men who lead girls astray. The aunt had always sided with her father.

Gwendoline was clearly moved by Pauline's explanation. 'My father has always neglected me,' she cried out.

Paul was defiant: 'My dictatorial father is not getting his way, he would disapprove of the way I'm not trying to make as much money as possible with my accountancy, I just try to enjoy myself, but I don't know yet how to.'

Then followed a firm assurance from George: 'My parents and my sisters used to be the judges of my life, now *I* choose my own way. My treatment has taught me to be independent of them.'

At this point Jane felt moved to admit: 'My mother has always ruled me and I have accepted her judgement. I feel so insecure.'

These interactions gave the attenders of this group a chance to benefit from each other's experiences. Parents prevent the development of a true self in their children in more than one way. Overprotection, possessiveness, neglect, dictatorial disapproval and ruling are all possible ways of crippling the self. After people have realized such influence, their conscience calls on them to establish their individual true self by resisting parental influences.

Interpretation 2: Empty Unsafe Life

Joan started the session with the following dream: 'I am leaving the office, in my hands I carry an empty saucepan. I return to the office because I had left my purse behind. I find the place unsafe, workmen are there, the lift is not working, the floorboards have been taken up.'

The following interpretation was offered: the empty saucepan stood for an empty life, the purse was symbolic of values for which the dreamer was searching. She had been in an unsatisfactory job for seven and a half years, now she was looking for a better job.

Pauline admitted: 'My life is empty. My parents have given me empty ideas, I am confused about values, I have missed the chance of getting married.'

Dan followed: 'I am looking for a life which is fulfilled, but I don't know whether I have the right ideas. Perhaps I use intellectual pursuits as an escape.'

These remarks stirred Richard to affirm his view on safety: 'It's money that counts. Wife and children are financial burdens.' Several members of the group expressed their strong disagreements with such a materialistic point of view.

Emptiness of life has been a central issue in this book. The crisis in valuation discussed epitomized in Chapter 1 epitomized the problem and contributions from Mannheim, Sennett and von Bertalanffy provided insight into its origin and extent. Joan's dream confronted her and those who were present at the group meeting with the challenge of how to cope with life's emptiness.

Interpretation 3: Relations with People

Richard's dream: 'A man has entered my room. I try to say to him: "What are you doing here?", but I cannot pronounce the words, I feel paralysed.'

Richard's own interpretation: 'The man is my neighbour in the room next to mine. He often disturbs me by being noisy, but I do not complain, as I am afraid of him. I imagine that he is my enemy, that he might go mad and might throw a knife through the thin partition between our rooms and might kill me. I consider people in general to be hostile and dangerous. I have never had a close friend, as I don't trust people, especially girls. They might entangle me in a marriage which would be only to their advantage, not to mine. I am frightened of people.'

This admission brought forth a response from Pauline: 'I don't think that people are my enemies, but I think they are selfish and therefore I don't trust them. I used to have faith in others, but they often disappointed me and let me down. Now I don't expect to have friends, I can't express my feelings of warmth, I am holding my emotions back which causes me to suffer.'

Gertrude had come to realize that the fault was hers: 'I could not bear a close relationship although I long for one.'

Rudolph associated Richard's dream with his main problem: 'My trouble is gambling and drinking. I have recently had a bad spell of gambling. As for drinking, it makes me more relaxed. Without a drink or two I can't face people, even at the office and I can't talk to them.'

Frederick told the group that he was not as isolated as Rudolph: 'I have men and women friends, but I have difficulties saying good-bye to them. I can't tear myself away from them.'

These remarks made George think of his problem with people: 'My problem is that I feel too soft. The others are hard, I don't dare approach them.'

Richard now realized that his feelings about himself and others agreed with George's: he also felt that he was too soft. His fear of others was of their hardness.

Jane spoke last: 'I have a boyfriend, but I don't want a sexual relationship with him and I don't want to get married. The responsibilities of a deep relationship frighten me.'

Discussion, art, especially patients' own paintings and drawings, and dream analysis were some of the methods, described earlier, that were employed in individual true-self psychotherapy. By applying them to group therapy, patients are given a chance of sharing each others' worlds and of reflecting on the significance of the experiences for their true selves.

This group treatment differs fundamentally from group analysis as practised by the psychoanalyst S H Foulkes.[246] His approach will now be viewed from the point of view of the true-self ethic.

PSYCHOANALYTIC GROUP TREATMENT

The group situation involves important modifications of psychoanalytical practice. The intense relationship between the psychoanalyst and the analysand is replaced by the relationship of the participants with each other and with the leader or conductor of the group. Accounts published by psychoanalytically minded group therapists, reveal successes without any evidence that psychoanalytical theory had been applied. Lonely, frightened people who have summoned the courage to join one of these groups are obviously helped by having been accepted by the group. It is, important to realize, however, that the psychoanalytical theory, although modified, is expressed, and its significance for the principles of the true-self ethic, this book's subject, must be clarified.

SCIENTIFIC ORIENTATION

No matter that critics have denied psychoanalysis a scientific status, this school was earlier classed as one of the sciences of the mind, as its representatives claim such a position and as the conceptual system bears the hallmark of natural science. Its outstanding characteristic is determinism, which means that there is no ethical freedom. People are considered to be the result of forces over which they have no control. It also means that there is a chain of cause and effect and, in the case of psychoanalysis, the cause of emotional disturbance in the adult is the result of early childhood experiences. Instinctual libido is postulated as the force, the dynamic – hence the spiritual love between people is reduced to sexual relations and people are turned into libidinal objects, losing their personal preciousness, as science cannot accommodate either individuality or personal freedom. The egoistic pleasure principle rules supreme in spite of evidence that hedonism brings about pain and not pleasure, and in spite of many examples of altruistic behaviour and attitude. Conscience, the central concern in true-self ethic, is turned into the superego which rules as the threatening authority of parent or society, demanding obedience.

Freud never practised group treatment but his mind, determined to find a scientific basis for social life, provided those of his followers who became group therapists with material.

The claim that human beings are bound to show 'primary hostility' to each other which has 'to be kept under control by a cultural super-ego' was earlier rejected (*see* pages 32–33).

The woman who broke down after her son's schizophrenic illness and who was admitted to a mental hospital and treated by a doctor who 'always tried to make her angry' considered that the doctor 'needed forgiving' (*see* page 68). But the doctor's guilt was that she had accepted the psychoanalytical view of aggressiveness as a primary instinct that must be expressed.

An example of the same nature comes from a hospital in which patients and the whole staff met regularly in group sessions. The majority of the staff accepted the Freudian view on the primary character of aggressiveness, expressed in anger.

The staff prided themselves on being open to the patients and on one occasion they informed them that on a certain day one of the psychiatrists, one of the social workers, one medical psychologist and one occupational therapist would not not attend the hospital. No reason for their absence was given. At the end of the meeting one member of staff suggested to the patients that they were very angry that they had been let down by so many important therapists who had deserted them.

As was the custom, the staff had a separate meeting afterwards. One opponent of psychoanalysis made a strong protest about the way the matter had been handled. He insisted that had the patients been told the reason for the absence of their therapists, there would not have been any reason to suspect anger. The reason was that they were all attending an important meeting of the Association of Mental Health. Had the patients been told that, they would have understood that the attendance would indirectly have been to their benefit. His colleagues admitted that they had provoked aggressiveness,[247] clearly in contradiction of the true-self ethic.

Foulkes clearly states that he accepts the Freudian view on the aggressive instinct[248] and we must assume that this view finds expression in the way he conducted groups and other psychoanalysts conduct their groups.

Two cases, taken from Foulkes' practice and reported in his book, suggest that patients were provoked to be aggressive after they had assimilated the dogma of primary aggression.

The first is a report of a woman member of a group who told the others that she was happily married, had a child and was functioning well 'all round'. 'She did her best to join in [the group]. Neverthless, the group was very annoyed with her for having no problems and some members were driven to fury. When pressed, she said that she had always liked her parents, both her father and her mother. This was never forgotten and she was never forgiven.'

Foulkes' own explanation of this outburst of anger is that patients experience cure as a threat. This is unconvincing; in a group run on true-self principles, patients support each other and would experience this woman's happiness as a source of strength for themselves.

The second case is that of a man who told the group that he had studied psychology which had helped him a great deal. 'This made the group furious, and their anger was not mitigated when he asserted that he had had plenty of problems, suffered from severe phobias, etc, and though one could help oneself to a certain degree, there were other aspects over which one needed help from other persons. At this point one of his neighbours [sitting near to him] pronounced that he would like to murder him. Another voiced her irritation and hatred in no uncertain terms.' One wonders why Foulkes had to 'slightly appease' the members of this group by 'reassuring them that this man had suffered a very severe breakdown lasting over two years – the sort of breakdown which some of them spent half their lives avoiding'.[249]

Why was it necessary to break a professional confidence (the man himself had not told the group of his severe breakdown!) and paint a picture to appeal for a little human sympathy? The fact that two members of the group became aggressive makes one assume that they all suffered from an acceptance of the dogma of primary aggressiveness.

This does not mean that we can deny the fact that people are aggressive. There is enough evidence; a rise in the amount of violence in our society, often provoked by disillusion and agitators. As was pointed out in relation to Freud's view on aggression, the true-self ethic relies on communal feelings, sympathy and love among people, helping them to face and transcend their aggression (*see* page 33).

We saw that in the account of a true-self group therapy, Bernard, who was suffering from paranoid schizophrenia, imagined that everybody was looking at him. He had to face his anger and aggressiveness, and say: 'I'm scared of people, but also afraid I might hit them.'

We heard from Jane that she was facing her sexual instinct, but decided that she did not want a sexual relationship with her boyfriend, as she was afraid of marriage and a 'deep relationship'.

In psychoanalytical group treatment, aggressiveness and sexuality are not interpreted as challenges, to be met by personal freedom, but as forces which determine human beings, conceived by objectifying science. In psychoanalytical group treatment, aggressiveness and sexuality are conceived as elements of people's social nature. In Foulkes's formulation, 'the infant–mother relationship is the first social relationship in the same sense as it is the first sexual and love relationship'.[250] But in the scientific framework, love cannot be understood as it is understood by Levinas who, we saw, insists that love aims at the other. But love is also fear for another and the strangeness of each other's worlds is one of mutual enjoyment which is personal and not universal, impersonal or libidinal. [251]

Scientific determinism is expressed in the assumption of inevitable causal relationships. S H Foulkes and E J Anthony have formulated the causal relations of neurotic illness: 'Psycho-analysis has shown that neuroses are based on conflict, conflict that arose early in life in relation to parents or their equivalents.' As group analysts, the authors maintain that 'this conflict, at bottom, is one between the individual's instinctive impulses and his group's cultural taboos [a reference to the punishment threatening cultural superego]'. Causality is followed up: the conflict 'becomes internalized, unconscious', its force represents 'the primary process', the assumed basic situation which involves patients and therapists. [252] The aim is to improve the capacity of the participants with regard to their social relationships.

In the earlier account of psychoanalysis, an American investigator was quoted as having found that 'psychotherapeutic change does not depend on the elucidation of historical antecedents [on cause-and-effect sequences] but on the reliving and modification of historically meaningful patterns that come alive in the patient–therapist relationship in vivo'(see page 33). Here we have the confirmation of the therapeutic fallacy of the scientific enterprise of Freud and his followers which involves regressing adult patients to childhood, depriving them of their adult ethical freedom, and which postulates that they have to become dependent on the transference situation on the therapist and in the group treatment on the group to target their infantile love and hate.

When the critical evaluation of dynamic psychotherapy was quoted, a contemporary philosopher-psychiatrist confirmed the fundamental mistake of the scientific approach of dynamic psychotherapies: insight into the alleged libidinal unconscious processes which have been made conscious does not lead to therapeutic change; only reflection effects change, which means that people have to make use of their ethical freedom to try to cope with instinctual or archetypal challenges.[253]

The rejection of dynamic psychotherapies on the grounds of comparison with controls (patients having no therapy) was not accepted, as intense contacts with a therapist could not have been totally ineffective. But the conclusion of the clinical evaluation must be accepted and Foulkes himself is very honest: psychoanalysis must admit that the scientific process is 'interminable'. An eminent analyst, Helene Deutsch, is quoted: 'We do not eliminate the original source of neurosis; we only help to achieve better ability to change neurotic frustrations into valid compensations.' This statement is made after 30 years of practice. One asks: 'what compensates for neurotic frustrations?' Foulkes acknowledges 'very severe obstacles to further therapeutic progress' and finally makes the confession: 'psychoanalysis cannot finally solve the problem of neurosis'. The true-self therapist goes further: he agrees with the critic of dynamic psychotherapy that this treatment is not helpful, but, moreover, is harmful because of its 'influence on patients' ethical and moral values – denying them the spiritual use of their ethical freedom. [254] But a tribute, paid earlier to doctors who use mechanistic scientific principles and to their helpers, including nurses, as well as to counsellors, must include psychotherapists who belong to different schools.

Through their theoretical preoccupation shines their spiritual humanity which benefits patients.

Professionals live in worlds which are different from the worlds of those whom they try to help. Why does their message fail to get across? Why do they fail in communication? This is the subject of our next enquiry, which is concerned with the test of selfhood in relations between doctors and patients.

12

DOCTOR–PATIENT
RELATIONSHIPS

———————————————— • ————————————————

John Kelly, an English professor of philosophy, has defined communication as a sharing of meaning.[255] Meanings are expressed in language. Doctors, like other professionals, have been trained to think in a technical language. Relations with their patients fail if they do not translate their language into the everyday language of their patients. People suffering from illnesses call on their doctors not only to provide treatment, but also to provide help in making their suffering meaningful, so that they can grasp its significance and cope with the malaise.

A number of situations in which communications have broken down are presented in preparation for the final chapter which elucidates how the true-self ethic can be shared by doctor and patient when they communicate successfully.

THE MEDICAL CLINICIAN

The following situations have been described as a personal view in the *British Medical Journal.*[256]

Parent of a child suffering from a severe deformity: 'I've got really depressed about this, doctor.'
Clinician leafs through the hospital case notes.
Parent (louder): 'I really have got very depressed about this, doctor.'
Clinician continues to leaf through the case notes.
Parent turns to husband: 'In fact, I've got so depressed, my doctor has put me on antidepressants, hasn't he, Dave?'
Clinician (after long interval): 'Well, I'm afraid that the hospital won't allow me to guarantee that I personally will do the operation although I usually do.'

The clinician closes the folder containing the case notes and silently hands the parent a slip of paper which means that the child has been put on the waiting list for the operation.

The mother in her world of anxiety about her sick child received no communication from this doctor who showed no willingness to enter into her world and to help her to make the experience of her child's illness meaningful. Instead, she received a message which ran like this: 'I have studied your child's case. I am not prepared to respond to your emotional state; by telling you that you cannot be sure that I shall perform the operation myself, I am cutting short any attempt to involve me personally.'

We may assume that this doctor is unpopular with the staff if he fails equally to communicate with them, being unaware of their feelings.

The writer of the personal view provides a further example of failed communication between another doctor and another parent of a very sick little girl:

Parent: 'You know, I simply can't manage her any more, I just can't cope.'
Clinician: No response.
Parent: 'In fact, I need someone to take her off my hands.'
Clinician: 'Well, Mrs Y, I feel sure that the sort of operation that I can do is unlikely to help your daughter.'

Again, there was no communication, no reply to the mother's distress which was greatly increased by the news that her child could not be helped by an operation. By thinking only in technical surgical terms, the doctor failed in his duty to assist people who have to cope with a relative's illness.

The writer of the personal view declares: 'I lost count of the number of distressed and angry parents [whose children suffer from severe deformities and who attend a hospital where special treatment may be offered] whose body language was a catalogue of Dantesque torment: flushing, coiling, writhing, losing eye contact [with people around them], the sheer physical tension and frustration, and grief of looking after disabled children. None of these physical signs [of the parents' distress, anger and disappointment] was picked up [by the insensitive doctors] or commented on.'[257]

The two examples demonstrate that the true-self ethic in medicine calls for communication with patients. If this is not forthcoming, doctors' selves are false and patients' selves cannot attain their truth in their suffering.

The next scenario presents a different situation: the sick child's father is a doctor himself, a young psychiatrist. This personal view thus refers to a doctor who is experiencing a patient's distress for which he needs professional help.

ON THE OTHER SIDE OF THE FENCE[258]

These are the circumstances: the child, a little girl of two-and-a-half, is suffering from a very severe attack of bronchial asthma which is life-threatening. The father is torn between two feelings: his private emotion of great anxiety for his child and his professional sense of duty not to lose control. The question is: how do the professional staff assist him in his struggle to preserve his dignity, his true self?

One of his colleagues failed him, as he explains: 'The doctor seems to be trying to put me or himself at ease by talking about medical schools. I am overwhelmingly preoccupied by my daughter and her breathing problem and do not want to talk about medical school. I feel my distress as the parent of a patient is being abnegated. I can see that he is trying to reassure me, but he is making me quite annoyed. I feel anxious that I should cover up my irritation, be a nice, calm relative. Again I collude with the polite chat.'

Not only did this hospital doctor fail to communicate with the distressed father, the general practitioner also failed. She was consulted when the child became much worse after discharge from hospital. So she recommended that the child should be taken back to the hospital. ' "Is this all right?"' she asked me. It seems as if she is worried that I am angry with her. I feel a need to reassure her and be polite. But am I not the one in distress? Things are getting complicated: I think that I am falling apart, but requests are being made of me as if I had autonomy [the freedom to act as a person, not weighed down by my anxiety].'

The hospital doctor in the casualty department rose to the occasion and her communication met the distressed father's need: 'She offers no reassurance. She speaks little and listens a lot. She is polite but there are no informalities. It seems a fitting approach considering how serious I think the situation is, and she is not expecting anything of me; she is taking control. She tells me. "Your daughter is not getting better despite all the treatments. Her history of needing to be ventilated last year is a worry. She needs to be in hospital." The result of this communication speaks for itself: I feel surprisingly calm.'

But the night nurse failed in her communication: 'It seems important to her that we [his wife and himself] like her. For her sake we have to be polite. This is difficult. I become uncomfortable when I notice that as we walk on to the ward, with our seriously sick child, we are all smiling.' Later, the same nurse made the father/doctor feel that he ought 'to be courteously grateful' for her attendance. 'That seemingly small demand fills me with resentment and rage. I reach a crescendo of anxiety. I am having to keep so many feelings under control and I am terrified what might happen if they break out. Disaster? Withdrawal of care from my daughter?'

The child got better and was discharged from hospital. The doctor explained his predicament on that day in hospital: 'Although this crisis was in my personal domain, it was lived out in hospital, which is my professional domain.' He admitted: 'My experience has changed the way I practise medicine.' He had learnt that 'it is important to try and understand the predicament and fears of patients. Some relief can be provided by trying to understand what is going on for them. At times of great distress it is correct to make clear and firm recommendations to patients and not to expect anything from them, not even a smile or a thank you. Why should they smile? Their experiences at these times are hideous.'

The last scenario is not concerned with a patient's or a patient's relative's experience, but with the question of how doctors should act in an emergency which, according to the author, allows for different decisions in an imagined situation.

DOCTOR: 'WHAT HAT SHOULD I WEAR?'[259]

The scene takes place in the casualty department that deals with accidents and emergencies. 'Irene rushes in, obviously in great distress. She stands unsteadily and her eyes are wide and wild. She exclaims: "I am going to kill myself, and I want as many people as I can to see me, and to know why I am killing myself." Then she explains: "Brian has been unfaithful. He's cheated on me. Not once but often and it's gone on for years now. I can't stand it any more. He treats me like dirt. He makes me feel worthless. All he cares about is himself and his own pleasure. I put everything into our marriage and I have nothing without it. But our marriage is nothing.

' "I don't want to live like this any longer. I want him to pay. I want him to suffer like I've suffered. It's his fault that I am going to kill myself, and I want him to feel the guilt." [She then turns to the people in the department]: "I want you to tell him that he has killed me."

'Now sobbing, Irene forces a handful of white pills into her mouth, opens a half-empty bottle of whisky, and swallows the pills.

'[Then] Irene sits down purposefully on a chair in the middle of the room and puts her head in her hands. She begins to rock gently forwards and back again.'

The writer assumes that different casualty doctors would respond to this situation differently and he describes their decisions using a suitable eponym to characterize their attitude.

'THE DOCTOR AS PURIST'

For the purist, 'a suicide attempt is not the concern of medical doctors'. Although the doctor knows that there is an effective antidote to the poison that Irene has swallowed, he does not try to administer it, as the patient does not wish to take it. He thinks that she should see a priest and should not waste a doctor's time which 'could be better spent working with people who wish to live'.

The writer has a further thought for the purist: by watching Irene's death, he might obtain 'useful scientific data, recording her physical and mental condition as she progresses towards unconsciousness'.

'THE DOCTOR AS MECHANIC'

He is a practical man who uses his knowledge of scientific medicine which deals with bodily mechanisms. He forces her to swallow the antidote and places her under nursing supervision to await psychiatric assessment.

'THE DOCTOR AS CARER'

Rather than forcing Irene to live, this type of doctor tries to 'counsel, support, and persuade her in a subtle way' to give up her suicidal decision. 'Through listening, talking and befriending, the Carer will hope to save her life.' He might become the mechanic if things become desperate.

'THE DOCTOR AS PUBLIC HEALTH GUARDIAN'

This type is only interested in programmes that deal with the health of the population and not in individuals. He advocates 'raising the price of tobacco and alcohol, rigorous screening programmes [to study the course of diseases], compulsory vaccination for school children, and preventive adult-education programmes designed to help people cope better should they ever feel suicidal'.

The author of this exercise is concerned with the question of how each of these doctors stands in relation to the law and his or her professional role. But in the context of our concern with the human relationship between doctors and their patients, our question is: what are Irene's needs from her doctor? These are far greater than the needs of the sick children's mothers whose needs were ignored by the purely clinically minded specialist and of the doctor–parent whose needs were not met by two of his colleagues and by the night nurse. These people, we can assume, were supported by their marriage partners who were mentioned (admittedly, the second mother's husband was not mentioned, but we can assume that he was with his wife). Although their selves were not respected as they should have been, they were not actually damaged. Therefore they were able to express their anger and frustration at the way the doctors had failed them. However, because Irene's husband had made her feel 'worthless', having treated her 'like dirt', she had lost her self and, therefore, the will to live.

If this is the correct diagnosis, the correct treatment is as follows: to make Irene feel the love which, in Levinas's words, aims at the Other – that is, a non-sexual love which does not expect or ask for anything in return; as the doctor–father said, no smile, no thank you should be expected. To quote Levinas again: 'The self that experiences the Other's love experiences itself lovable', which, in Irene's case, means that her self-respect and her selfhood are restored and with that her will to live. Her need would have been met.

As love is never a stereotype, Irene's doctor has to find his way of expressing medical love which occurs spontaneously and is manifest in the tone of his voice and perhaps in the way he touches her shoulder. As a nurse who was deeply moved by Irene's plight was present, the doctor might gain help from her. She could be the doctor's assistant by putting her arm around Irene's shoulders – one woman comforting another woman.

Irene's self would respond quickly to this antidote to the poison of her marriage. She would not have to be forced to swallow the medicinal antidote (in any case you cannot force people to open their mouths and swallow anything if they are unwilling to do so). If she required treatment to restore her true self, she should be offered true-self psychotherapy as described on page 57, and she would swallow it willingly.

Seen from the watchtower of applied medical true-self ethic, the doctors who wear the hats of the purist, mechanic and public health guardian appear as caricatures, unfit for the task in hand. The doctor as carer is right in listening and supporting Irene, but not in trying to use persuasion and in befriending her, as this is likely to lead to personal involvement and dependency.

13

LIBERATING MEDICINE

—————————————— • ——————————————

Irene's suicidal attempt is discussed in David Seedhouse's book *Liberating Medicine*.[260] This is also the title of the final chapter of our thesis. We shall explore the significance of Seedhouse's view in the light of the view expressed in this volume. According to Seedhouse, 'doctors require general problem-solving abilities. And above this doctors need the *perspective of curiosity*'. A 'constantly critical attitude' is required and 'a constant questioning,[261] in order to deal best with the broader difficulties of life which confront them'. Seedhouse stresses the fact that doctors face the uncertainty of interpretation and in his book provides an illustration of this problem: a young girl's refusal to eat properly which has led to a dangerous loss of weight. The question is whether she is suffering from the life-threatening condition called anorexia nervosa, and the doctor has to choose between forcing her to eat or helping her to face her problems with more confidence than she has. One of the doctor's dilemmas is the question of whether the girl should be pronounced 'ill' while she denies that there is anything the matter with her. Should not her wish to be very thin be respected? Has the doctor the right to insist on treatment under the present circumstances?[262]

As was the case in Irene's attempted suicide, the 'ethical uncertainty' only arises for the doctor who doubts which medical model, the purist's or the mechanic's or the carer's he ought to adopt. Those who consider as basic the patient's concern with his or her interpretation of the true-self ethic, do not agree that medicine's 'category mistake' consists of being 'trapped by both semantics and social convention'.[263]

Doctors who trust their patients' conscience see their own duty to try to help them to reach the decision which their true selves demand, irrespective of convention and they never consider it a semantic matter. The medical labels which Seedhouse discusses at length (disease or not disease) are irrelevant and grossly misleading. Those who have faith in the true-self ethic would never raise the question whether those who suffer from uncertainty about their true self should be classified as bearers of 'mental events'.[264]

The discussion on health, which occupies more than six pages in Seedhouse's book[265] reveals the difference between his attitude and the message from this volume: Seedhouse tries to find a definition that satisfies those who work professionally for people's health. He discusses the theories of what constitutes health and gets involved in the question of whether disease must be classified as an obstacle to health.

The shackles which restrict medicine are derived from the spirit of our age: a one-sided reliance on science and technology. There is no doubt that such reliance is justified and necessary in the case of medicine, but its postulate of inevitability (determinism) and its necessary ignoring of individuality (uniqueness of the person) call for liberation from science's exclusive reign. This involves a call for liberation from the arrogance of those who consider that scientific methods have a monopoly in medicine and that all alternative forms of treatment must submit to scientific scrutiny.

Scientists must abandon the claim that the holistic approach can be reduced to the mechanistic scientific approach. Such liberation is fundamental. It frees spiritual and biological holism, although both were admitted to have limitations which call for the employment of science – for instance, of drug treatment. In such cases it is conceded that the methods of Natural Therapy do not evoke a curative response in cases of bodily ailment, nor do the methods of true-self psychotherapy evoke a curative response in every case of psychiatric ailment.

This admission in no way justifies the claim that all emotional distress must be the object of the sciences of the mind which identify the cerebral, archetypal, libidinal, reflex-type and social forces which are treated by their methods. Details of this claim and the call for liberation from the scientific dogma are provided in the text and the way of restoring the acknowledgement of spiritual ethical freedom is indicated: an appeal to people's freedom to face these forces and attempt to cope with them.

Such an exercise in personal ethical freedom is made unnecessarily difficult if patients are treated by clinicians who consider them only as bearers of diseases. Medicine must be liberated from such insensitivity and from the hedonistic ethic which only recognizes a striving for pleasure. The domain of the self-centred interpretation of the true-self ethic must be increased to incorporate Levinas's ethic which is concerned with the self and the Other.

Seedhouse also considers ethics to be of fundamental importance for medicine, but his interpretation differs basically from our true-self ethic, and because of this difference he fails to liberate medicine. Seedhouse is concerned with the type of moral conflict which we decided earlier not to make our ethical concern: questions of whether doctors should oblige women who ask for a termination of their pregnancy, or others who claim that they are entitled to employ surrogate mothers, or whether they should perform euthanasia or to withhold life-supporting measures from terminally ill patients. The reason why these questions were excluded was that each doctor must decide what is right in such circumstances (*see* page 7). In such cases it is the medical practitioners and not the patients who are faced with an ethical conflict which they are expected to solve. The true-self ethic, on the other hand, expects doctors to help patients to find a true answer to *their* ethical problems. Seedhouse's ethical example is that of a girl of 15 who asks her GP for a prescription of the contraceptive pill. The girl is sure what is right for her and the doctor has to find his right answer.[266]

In the case of the heroin addict who is not prepared to change his or her injection habit, the doctor is not charged to enable the patient to discover his or her true self as the addict – at least at the present stage – is not seeking for a true self apart from his or her addiction. As Seedhouse indicates, the same person may be open to a change of attitude should he or she seek help when intoxicated.[267] Then the doctor ought to try to help the patient to find his or her true self.

Seedhouse identifies a true self with a healthy self and he asks doctors to respect their patients' autonomy, their right to decide against a treatment which leaves them unbearably crippled. Seedhouse argues that, in such a case, doctors should not 'create autonomy', which means creating situations in which patients have to endure a restricted freedom.

A case which illustrates Seedhouse's point is the following: 'Dax was horribly burnt, left blind and without parts of his hands. He wished to die, but his doctors decided that he should live and saved his life. He spends his time studying and speaking to "medical ethics" audiences arguing that he should have been allowed to die.'

From the point of view of the true-self ethic, Dax's complaint is unjustified. The doctors did their duty and if Dax is not prepared to live in his very reduced state of health, he can commit suicide. He may need help to bear his crippled state and a doctor who accepts the true-self ethic would try to provide such help.

To the true-self therapist, health and ill health are not fixed entities, they are challenges to people's freedom.

Seedhouse makes no allowance for meeting these challenges. He argues that it is a 'category mistake in medicine' to create a state of health against the patient's wish. But doctors must take into consideration that it was not the patient's last wish. The fact that Dax did not commit suicide proves that point, even if he tells his audiences that the doctors ought to have respected his wish to die. This wish was expressed by a man who was in excruciating pain after having suffered extensive burns. When he realized the extent of his injuries, he told the doctors to let him die. Seedhouse makes no allowance for Dax's state of mind; he only states that he was not mentally ill and was rational. He implies that doctors ought not to take into consideration the turmoil in the mind of a patient who finds himself in such a predicament. He expects doctors to weigh up possible human priorities with their patients and act accordingly. But Dax was in no position at the time of seeing the doctors to make such a balanced decision.

He obviously changed his attitude and co-operated with his doctors during the months when he endured the treatment which involved plastic surgery. We must assume that during that period he showed great courage – a manifestation of personal freedom, of autonomy. He may well have said at times 'Stop the treatment, it is not worthwhile', but in reality he accepted it, and the doctors rightly did not stop. Seedhouse argues that if 'stop' is 'thought through', a patient's wish must be respected. But 'thinking through' is not possible when a patient is in agony.[268]

Seedhouse admits that the autonomy test does not 'go into detailed ethical analysis, makes no claim to depth – it is a litmus test, it is a traffic light: should I stop or should I go?'[269] This admission and the comparison with the traffic light reveals the flaw in the autonomy test and the need for the doctor to reject Seedhouse's test. They must accept Levinas's interpretation of their relations with their patients as ethical. Dax's disfigured and blind face conveys to his doctors the idea of human infinity, of human possibilities, of losing and regaining the courage to live. As Levinas said, the face-to-face relation is 'an irreducible relation'; it certainly cannot be reduced to the relation a car driver has with the traffic light. He stops automatically when the light is red. Doctors, who may be asked to stop life-saving treatment when a patient is suffering agony, must interpret this request as coming from a soul which is struggling with the mystery of life and death.

Seedhouse believes that doctors need to be liberated from wrong attitudes which are the result of faulty medical education. He singles out two aspects of medical practice where such liberation is essential. One is concerned with the uncertainty which plays an important part in the diagnosis and treatment of diseases. Anorexia nervosa is a case in point.

The holistic physician realizes that the way in which scientific medicine classifies patients as bearers of specific diseases leads to such uncertainties.

From the holistic point of view this problem does not arise, as patients are not categorized from a mechanistic objective point of view but as sick people whose treatment consists of a change in their subjective lifestyle with the addition of methods that do not interfere with the natural healing process but that promote this process: homoeopathic medicines, acupuncture, osteopathy and chiropractic providing such assistance. It was admitted that this form of medicine has its own uncertainty and that therefore scientific medicine must be held in readiness.

Autonomy is a manifestation of true selfhood, which means that people meet the demands of their conscience and that medical doctors and their helpers are liberated, freed from the wrong attitudes of mechanistic science and from Seedhouse's rationalistic interpretation of patients' selfhood and from his preoccupation with medical models. Autonomy, which is related to patients' true selfhood, requires doctors to make themselves responsible for the relationship with their patients, to see in the patient the Other in Levinas's sense, the Other struggling with doubts and fears. Seedhouse quotes the cases of patients whose autonomy was not respected. One woman, for example, was not given the choice between two types of operation for breast cancer,[270] but he omits to consider the woman's need for help to come to terms with the threat to her life, which is the primary concern before the question of a radical or less radical operation can be decided. An open communication with the doctor is required to come to terms with the terror of death from a cancer which might spread throughout the body.

Seedhouse warns against assuming a 'diminished autonomy' in the case of a young woman who was admitted to a mental hospital after having been caught shoplifting, getting drunk and complaining of feeling lethargic. She was injected with a drug to steady her disturbed emotional state, but was not told of the possible side-effects of the treatment. Seedhouse argues that this patient ought to have been given the chance to agree to the treatment that should have been explained to her.[271]

From the true-self point of view, a far more important matter is ignored: she was blamed by her family for having caused a lot of trouble. She was unemployed and her father was terminally ill. Although she was intelligent, she drifted away from school before taking her A-level examinations which would have given her the chance of a fulfilling job. She could not concentrate, and could not see the relevance of trying to do anything. She was 'depressed', which was hardly surprising, and the situation did not call for an injection, to calm her down.

From the true-self ethic point of view, her autonomy was indeed diminished. She did not feel free to lead her life as her conscience expected it. The true-self therapist would have to help her to find her way, which would not be a matter of explaining the side-effects of the injection, but would require a far more responsible attitude towards the doctor–patient relationship, and would take much longer, than the one advocated by Seedhouse.

If we mean by an autonomous self one that is sure of itself, we must recognize the crisis in valuation of our present society to be a powerful destabilizing force, depriving people of their autonomy. The sociologists Mannheim and Sennett and the biologist von Bertalanffy were quoted as interpreters of the anti-autonomical powers in our society, creating protean selves without an innate core, deprived of their essential symbolic universe. We saw as the results the rise of drug addiction, suicides, mental illness, the flight into anonymity and delinquency, the symptoms of the spiritual social malaise. Indifference to bodily health, which are evident in such destructive habits as smoking, excessive drinking and wrong eating habits, are further symptoms. The true-self ethic is offered as an antidote. It includes the ethical relation between the self and the Other, which is accepted tacitly by people in general, and practised explicitly as true-self psychotherapy for individuals and for groups of patients, and Natural Therapy which includes an appeal to people's freedom of conscience. In this way not only medicine may be liberated but also all those who, as actual or potential patients, seek autonomous selfhood.

NOTES

———————————— • ————————————

INTRODUCTION

0 Ledermann, E K, *Mental Health and Human Conscience, the true and the false self*, Gower Publishing Co, Avebury, 1984

CHAPTER 1

1 Jaspers, Karl, *The Origins and Goal of History*, Routledge & Kegan Paul, London, 1953, p 154

2 Buber, Martin, *The Knowledge of Man*, George Allen & Unwin, London, 1965, p 134

3 Buber, Martin, *I and Thou*, 2nd edn, T & T Clark, Edinburgh, 1959, p 34

4 Goethe, Johann Wolfgang von, *Faust: A Tragedy*, translated by B Taylor, Frederick Warne & Co, London, p 150, no date of publication given

5 Barnard, David, 'Love and Death: Existential Dimensions of Physicians' Difficulties with Moral Problems', *The Journal of Medicine and Philosophy*, vol 13, no 4, November 1988, p 398

6 Heinemann, Fritz, 'Ethik' in *Die Philosophie im XX. Jahrhundert, Eine Enzyklopaedische Darstellung Ihrer Geschichte, Disziplinen und Aufgaben,* Herausgegeben von Fritz Heinemann, Oxford, Ernst Klett Verlag, 1959, pp 458–61

7 Sartre, Jean-Paul, *Existentialism and Humanism*, Methuen & Co, London, 1948, pp 35–37

8 Mason, P and Wilkinson, G 'The prevalence of psychiatric morbidity in Great Britain', *The British Journal of Psychiatry*, January 1996, vol 168, pp 1–3

9 '2 million children mentally ill' *Mims Magazine Weekly*, September 1993

10 Graham, Philip and Hughes, Carol, *So Young, So Sad, So Listen*, Publications Department, Royal College of Psychiatrists, 17 Belgrave Square, London SW1X 8PG, 1995

11 'Britain's 50,000 heroin addicts. The people who believe they'd never get hooked', *The Listener*, 10 January 1985, pp 10–12

12 Macdonald, Donald Ian, 'Drugs, Drinking and Adolescence', *American Journal of Diseases of Children*, vol 138, no 2, February 1984, pp 117–25

13 Segal, Bernard, 'Psychological Aspects of Drug-taking Behaviour', *The International Journal of Addictions*, vol 18, no 5, 1983, p 612

14 Galizio, Mark and Stein, Flo S, 'Sensation-seeking and Drug Choice', *The International Journal of Addictions*, vol 18, no 8, 1983, pp 1039–48

15 Nicholl, Armand M Jr, 'The Nontherapeutic Use of Psychoactive Drugs, A Modern Epidemic', *The New England Journal of Medicine*, vol 308, no 16, 21 April 1983, pp 925–32

16 Szasz, Thomas, *Ceremonial Chemistry, The Ritual Persecution of Drugs, Addicts, and Pushers*, Routledge & Kegan Paul, London, 1975, pp 43,44

17 Petzel, Sue V and Riddle, Mary, 'Adolescent Suicide: Psychological and Cognitive Aspects', *Adolescent Psychiatry*, no 9, 1981, p 343

18 *Ibid*, p 344

19 *Ibid*, p 344

20 *Ibid*, p 350

21 *Ibid*, p 352

22 *Ibid*, p 361

23 *Ibid*, p 363

24 *Ibid*, p 371

25 Miller, Derek, 'Adolescent Suicide: Etiology and Treatment', *Adolescent Psychiatry*, no 9, 1981, p 340

26 'Epidemiology of suicides in Northern Ireland 1984–1989', *Irish Journal of Medical Science*, vol 160, no 11, p 354–57, November 1991

27 Fields, Donald, 'Suicides rise as Norway grows richer', *The Sunday Times,* 17 November 1985, p 19

28 World Health Organization, Annual Statistics 1988, p 295

29 'Suicide in Norway. Changes in the 20th century with special emphasis on the development during the last 20 years', *Tidskrift For Den Norske Laegeforening*, vol 112, no 1, pp 38–42, 10 January 1992

30 Suokas, J and Lonnqvist, J, 'Outcome of attempted suicide and psychiatric consultations: risk factors and suicide mortality during five-year follow-up', *Acta Psychiatrica Scandinavica*, vol 84, no 6, pp 545–49, December 1991

31 *The Status and Trends of The Global HIV/AIDS Pandemic*, Final Report, XI International Conference on AIDS, Vancouver, 7–12 July 1996

32 Fromm, Erich, *The Art of Loving*, George Allen and Unwin London, 1957, pp. 89, 54, 55

33 Mannheim, Karl, *Diagnosis of Our Time, Wartime Essays of a Sociologist*, Kegan Paul, Trench, Trubner & Co, London, 1943

34 *Ibid*, p 25

35 Sennett, Richard, 'Destructive Gemeinschaft' in *Beyond the Crisis*, ed Norman Birnbaum, Oxford University Press, New York, 1977, pp 180, 181

36 von Bertalanffy, Ludwig, 'Human Values in a Changing World', in *New Knowledge in Human Values*, ed Abraham H Maslow, Harper & Row, New York, 1959, p 68

37 *Ibid*, pp 70, 71, 72, 73, 74

38 Tillich, Paul, 'Is a Science of Human Value Possible?' in *New Knowledge in Human Values*, p 196

CHAPTER 2

39 Sargant, William, *The Unquiet Mind*, William Heinemann, London, reprinted 1984, p 196

40 Trethowan, W H, 'From straitjackets to Soma', *World Medicine*, 16 June 1979, p 28

41 Jaspers K, *Philosophie*, Springer-Verlag, Berlin, Göttingen and Heidelberg, 1948, p 874

42 MacKay, Donald M, 'The bankruptcy of determinism', *New Scientist*, 2 July 1970, p 24

43 *Ibid*, pp 24, 25

44 Straus, Erwin W, 'The Sense of the Senses', *Southern Journal of Philosophy*, winter 1965, pp 192,193

45 Kant, Immanuel, *Critique of Pure Reason*, translated by Norman Kemp Smith, MacMillan & Co, London, 1929, pp 359–60

46 Marcel, Gabriel, 'On the Ontological Mystery' in *The Philosophy of Existence*, The Harvill Press, London, 1948, p 8

47 Chesser, Eustace S, 'Behaviour Therapy: Recent Trends and Current Practice', *British Journal of Psychiatry*, 1976, vol 129, p 293

48 *Ibid*, p 295

49 This is the account of cognitive psychotherapy by two psychiatrists, Richard S Stern and Lynne M Drummond, working in a London hospital. Their book *The Practice of Behavioural and Cognitive Psychotherapy* was published by Cambridge University Press, Cambridge, in 1991

50 Dewhurst, David, 'How Can I Know Myself?', Philosophy, *The Journal of the Royal Institute of Philosophy*, 1984, vol 59, no 228, pp 210, 215

51 Freud, S, *Group Psychology and the Analysis of the Ego*, The Hogarth Press and the Institute of Psycho-Analysis, London, vol 19, 1955, p 90

52 Kohurt, Heinz, *The Analysis of the Self, A Systematic Approach to the Psychoanalytic Treatment of Narcissistic Personality Disorders*, The Hogarth Press for the Institute of Psycho-analysis, London, 1971, p 40

53 Polanyi, Michael, *Personal Knowledge, Towards a Post-Critical Philosophy*, Routledge & Kegan Paul, London, 1958, p 309

54 Frankl, Viktor E, 'Der unbewusste Gott', in *Das Gewissen als Problem*, Amandus Verlag, Vienna, 1949, pp 270–72

55 Jones, David H, 'Freud's Theory of Moral Conscience', Philosophy, *The Journal of the Royal Institute of Philosophy*, 1966, vol XLI, no 155, p 43

56 *Ibid*, p 56

57 Freud, S, *Civilization and its Discontents*, 3rd edn, The Hogarth Press and The Institute of Psycho-analysis, London, 1946, pp 86, 137, 139

58 Guntrip, Harry, *Personality Structure and Human Interaction, The Developing Synthesis of Psychodynamic Theory*, The Hogarth Press and The Institute of Psycho-Analysis, London, 1961, pp 279, 287, 316

59 Strupp, H H, 'A Reformulation of the Dynamics of the Therapist's Contribution', in *Effective Psychotherapy, A Handbook of Research*, Pergamon Press, USA, 1977, ch 1, pp 17, 20

60 Mitchell, Kevin M, *et al*, 'A Reappraisal of the Therapeutic Effectiveness of Accurate Empathy, Nonpossessive Warmth and Genuineness', in *Effective Psychotherapy*, Pergamon Press, USA, 1977, ch 18, p 491

61 Garfield, L, 'Research in the Training of Professional Psychotherapists', in *Effective Psychotherapy*, Pergamon Press, USA, 1977, ch 4

62 Fenichel, O, *The Psychoanalytic Theory of Neurosis*, W W Norton & Co. New York, 1945, p 4

63 Casement, Patrick, 'Interpretation: Fresh Insight or Cliché?', *Bulletin*, The British Association of Psychotherapists, no 17, July 1986, pp 6, 7

64 Fenichel, O, *op cit*, p 38

65 Fordham, Frieda, *An Introduction to Jung's Psychology*, Pelican Books, London, 1953, p 27

66 *Ibid*, p 28

67 Jung, C G, *Memoirs, Dreams, Reflections*, recorded and edited by Aniela Jaffe, Routledge & Kegan Paul, London, 1953, p 17

68 Jung, C G, *The Integration of the Personality*, Kegan Paul, Trench, Trubner & Co, London, 1940, p 80

69 *Ibid*, pp 80, 81

70 Fordham, Frieda, *op cit*, pp 49, 50

71 Jacobi, Jolan, *The Psychology of C G Jung, An Introduction with Illustrations*, Kegan Paul, Trench, Trubner & Co, London, 1942, p 57

72 Andrews, Gavin, 'The Essential Psychotherapies', *British Journal of Psychiatry*, 1993, no 162, pp 447–51

73 Heaton, J M, 'Insight into Phenomenology and Psychoanalysis', *Journal of the British Society for Phenomenology*, vol 3, no 2, May 1972, pp 135–45.

74 Andrews, Gavin, *op cit*, p 448

75 Perls, Frederick S, Hefferline, Ralph F, Goodman, Paul, *Gestalt Therapy, Excitement and Growth in the Human Personality*, Souvenir Press, p 373

76 *Ibid*, p 74

77 *Ibid*, pp 220, 340, 341, 342

78 Marteau, Louis, 'Encounter and the New Therapies', *British Journal of Hospital Medicine*, March 1976, p 264.

79 Ansbacher, Heinz L, and Ansbacher, Rowena R, *The Individual Psychology of Alfred Adler, A Systematic Presentation in Selection from his Writings*, Basic Books, New York, 1956, p 423

80 *Ibid*, pp 361, 363

81 *Ibid*, p 364

82 *Ibid*, pp 397, 398

83 Silverman, Hugh J, 'Merleau-Ponty's Human Ambiguity', *Journal of the British Society for Phenomenology*, vol 10, no 1, January 1979, p 29

84 Schweitzer, Albert, *Civilization and Ethics*, 3rd edn, Adam & Charles Black, London, 1946, p 214

CHAPTER 3

85 King, Magda, *Heidegger's Philosophy, A Guide to his Basic Thought*, Delta Books, New York, 1964, pp 112–114

86 Heidegger, Martin, *Being and Time*, SCM Press, London, 1962, pp 213–19

87 *Ibid*, pp 313–16

88 *Ibid*, pp 302,311

89 Laing, R D and Cooper, D G, *Reason and Violence, A Decade of Sartre's Philosophy*, Tavistock Publications, London, 1964, pp 119,120

90 Jaspers, Karl, *Philosophie*, 2nd edn, Springer-Verlag, Berlin, Göttingen and Heidelberg,1948, pp 370, 372

91 Scheler, Max, 'Reue und Wiedergeburt', Bd 1, *Gesammelte Werke*, Francke Verlag, Bern, 1954, p 36

92 *Ibid*, p 42

93 *Ibid*, p 47

94 Rowe, Dorothy, *Depression, the way out of your prison*, Routledge & Kegan Paul, London, 1983, p 127

95 *Ibid*, p 126

96 Ryan, C and Ryan, K M, *A Private Battle*, Simon & Schuster, New York, 1979

97 Hawkins, Anne, 'Two Pathographies: A Study in Illness and Literature', *The Journal of Medicine and Philosophy*, August 1984, vol 9, no 3

98 *Ibid*, p 239

99 *Ibid*, p 241

100 *Ibid*, p 242

101 *Ibid*, p 246

102 *Ibid*, p 248

103 *Ibid*, p 249

104 Pastorelli, France, *The Glorious Bondage of Illness*, English translation, George Allen & Unwin, London, 1936

105 *Ibid*, p 29

106 *Ibid*, p 31

107 *Ibid*, p 108

108 *Ibid*, p 155

109 *Ibid*, p 183

110 *Ibid*, p 99

111 Simenon, Georges, *The Patient*, Hamish Hamilton, London, 1963

112 *Ibid*, p 3

113 *Ibid*, p 29

114 *Ibid*, p 36

115 *Ibid*, pp 43,45

116 *Ibid*, p 93

117 *Ibid*, p 97

118 *Ibid*, p 133

119 *Ibid*, p 142

120 *Ibid*, p 236

121 *Ibid*, p 236

122 Kübler-Ross, Elizabeth, 'Dying – From the Patient's Point of View', *Triangle*, vol 13, no 1, 1974, pp 25–26

123 *Ibid*, p 26

124 Gautam, S and Nijhawan, M, 'Communicating with Cancer Patients', *The British Journal of Psychiatry*, no 150, June 1987, pp 761, 764

CHAPTER 4

125 Cassirer, Ernst, *An Essay on Man, An Introduction of a Philosophy of Human Culture*, Yale University, USA, 1944, p 143

126 *Ibid*, p 161

CONCLUSION TO PART I

127 Blackham, H J, *Six Existentialist Thinkers*, Routledge & Kegan Paul, London, 1952, p 3

128 Roberts, David E, *Existentialism and Religious Belief*, A Galaxy Book, Oxford University Press, New York, 1959, pp 6, 7

129 *Ibid*, p 7

130 Collingwood, R G, *Speculum Mentis or The Map of Knowledge*, Clarendon Press, Oxford, 1924, p 166

131 Roberts, David E, *op cit*, pp 7, 8

132 *Ibid*, p 8

CHAPTER 5

133 Dawkins, Richard, *The Blind Watchmaker*, Longman, UK, 1986, p 3

134 *Ibid*, p 111

135 *Ibid*, p 120

136 *Ibid*, p 116

137 Weiss, Paul A, 'The living system: determinism stratified', in *Beyond Reductionism, The Alpach Symposium, New perspectives in the life sciences*, eds Arthur Koestler and J R Smythies, Radius Books, Hutchinson, London, 1972, p 37

138 *Ibid*, p 36

139 *Ibid*, p 36

140 *Ibid*, p 37

141 Woodger, J H, *Biological Principles, A Critical Study*, Kegan Paul, Trubner & Co, London, 1929, pp 242, 310

CHAPTER 6

142 Walters, A Harry, *Ecology, Food & Civilisation*, Charles Knight, London 1973, p 177

143 Bellinger, A *et al*, 'Low-level lead exposures and early development in socioeconomically disadvantaged children', (abstract), Edinburgh Workshop, quoted in Adam Markham, *The Perils of Vehicle Emissions*, Friends of the Earth, London, July 1987, p 22

144 Russel-Jones, R, 'The health effect of vehicle emissions' quoted in Markham, *op cit*, Friends of the Earth, London, p 22

145 'Americans overdose ozone', *New Scientist*, 22 July 1989, p 21

146 Holman, C, 'Air Pollution from Diesel Vehicles', Friends of the Earth, London, July 1987, p 23

147 'Bad diet ruining America's health', *The Independent*, 28 July 1988, p 8

148 Muir, C S and Parkin, D M, 'The world cancer burden: prevent or perish', *British Medical Journal*, vol 290, 5 January 1985, p 55

149 Moxham, J, 'Join the fight to stub out smoking epidemic', *Doctor*, 21 November 1991, p 54

150 *British Medical Bulletin*, 1996, vol 52, no 1, p 12

151 Newcomb, P A and Carbone P P, 'The health consequences of smoking', *Journal: Medical Clinics of North America*, vol 76, no 2, pp 305–31, March 1992

152 Arya, S N, Rajiv, K and Arya, S, 'Hazards of Smoking', *Journal of the Indian Medical Association*, vol 89, no 4, pp 98–100, April 1991

153 Zetterström, O *et al*, 'Another smoking hazard: raised Serum IgE concentration and increased risk of occupational allergy', *British Medical Journal*, vol 283, 7 November 1971, pp 1215–17

154 Cummins, Richard O *et al*, 'Smoking and drinking by middle-aged British men: effects of social class and town of residence', *British Medical Journal*, vol 283, 5 December 1981, pp 1497–1502

155 Small, P *et al*, 'Alcohol dependence and phobic anxiety states: a prevalence study', *British Journal of Psychiatry*, vol 144, January 1984, p 53

156 Annual Report of the Chief Medical Officer 1990, Great Britain

157 'Alcohol in industry', *British Medical Journal*, vol 294, 21 February 1987, p 460

158 Steele, D W, 'Social aspects of alcohol', *Medicine International*, March 1985, p 659

159 McGee, James O'Donnell, 'The pathology of alcohol induced disease', *ibid*, p 652

160 'Alcoholism: new evidence for a genetic contribution', *British Medical Journal*, vol 284, no 6323, 17 April 1982, p 1137

161 Chick, Jonathan, 'Do alcoholics recover?', *British Medical Journal*, vol 285, 3 July 1982, pp 3,4

162 Laurence, D R and Bennett, P N, *Clinical Pharmacology*, Churchill Livingstone, Edinburgh and London, 1980, pp 538,539

163 Greden, John F, 'Caffeinism: A Diagnostic Dilemma', *American Journal of Psychiatry*, vol 131, no 10, October 1974, pp 1089–92

164 Farcas, C S, 'Tea and iron-deficiency anaemia', letter, *British Medical Journal*, 23 February 1980

165 Arnesen, E *et al*, 'Coffee and serum cholesterol', *British Medical Journal*, vol 288, 30 June 1984, p 1960

166 Tang, D *et al*, 'Caffeine and babies', *British Medical Journal*, vol 299, 8 July 1989, p 121

167 *American Journal of Obstetrics and Gynaecology*, 1986, no 154, pp 14–20, report in 'News and Notes, Views', *British Medical Journal*, vol 292, 22 March 1986, p 831

168 Atkins, Elisha, 'Fever-New Perspectives on an Old Phenomenon', *The New England Journal of Medicine*, vol 308, no 16, 1983, pp 958–59

169 Dunnell, Karen, and Cartwright, Ann, *Medicine Takers, Prescribers and Hoarders*, Routledge & Kegan Paul, London, 1972, pp 22,45

170 'The Magic Pill', leading article, *GP*, November 1965, p 4

171 Kielsden, Jens *et al*, 'Controlled trial of fasting and one-year vegetarian diet in rheumatoid arthritis', *The Lancet*, vol 338, no 8772, 12 October 1991, pp 899–902. This article reports on the use of the scientific control method to prove the efficacy of the Natural Therapy approach with regard to diet, ignoring the scientific dietetic principle. It represents an important development in the recognition of Natural Therapy.

172 Simon, Gary L *et al*, 'The Human Intestinal Microflora', *Digestive Diseases and Sciences*, vol 31, no 9, September 1986, supplement, pp 1475–625

173 The illustrations are from Neill, Charles A, *Poise and Relaxation*, a Family Doctor Publication, London (now out of print), no year of publication stated

174 Schultz, Johannes H, and Luthe, Wolfgang, *Autogenic Training, a Psychophysiological Approach in Psychotherapy*, Grune & Stratton, New York, 1959

175 Reilly D, Taylor M, *et al*, 'Is Homoeopathy a Placebo Response? Controlled Trial of Homoeopathic Potency with Pollen in Hayfever as Model', *The Lancet*, vol 2, 18 October 1986, pp 881–86

176 Rubik, Beverley, 'Report on the status of homoeopathy with recommendations for future research', *British Homoeopathic Journal*, vol LXXVIII, April
1989, p 88

177 Ledermann, E K, 'Homoeopathy and Natural Therapeutics', *The British
Homoeopathic Journal*, vol XXXV, no 1, May 1945, pp 31, 34

178 Hahnemann, Samuel, *Organon of the Rational Art of Healing*, J M Dent &
Sons, London, E P Dutton & Co, New York, 1913, p 90

179 *Ibid*, p 94

180 Ledermann, E K, 'Body, Mind and Spirit', *The British Homoeopathic Journal*,
vol L, no 4, October 1961

181 Ledermann, E K, 'Homoeopathy, and the existential–phenomenological
approach', *The British Homoeopathic Journal*, vol LV no 1, January 1966

182 Ledermann, E K, 'The patient's experience and the homoeopathic drug
picture', *The British Homoeopathic Journal*, vol LVI, no 2, April 1967

183 See, for instance; Campbell, Anthony, *Acupuncture, the modern scientific
approach*, Faber & Faber, 1987

184 For an account of natural therapy and its allies, see, for instance, Ledermann,
E K, *Your Health In Your Hands, A Case for Natural Medicine*, Green Books,
Totnes, 1989 The emphasis is on the patients' responsibility for their health.

CHAPTER 7

185 Pearson, Richard, 'Overuse injuries in musicians', letter, *British Medical
Journal*, vol 298, 3 June 1989, p 1517

186 Bird, Howard, 'Overuse injuries in musicians', *British Medical Journal*, vol
298, 29 April 1989, p 1129

187 Dickson, Joan, 'Overuse injuries in musicians', letter, *British Medical Journal*,
vol 298, 3 June 1989, p 1517

188 *See* Ledermann, E K, 'Holistic Treatment of Musicians' Aches', *International
Society for the Study of Tension in Performance (ISSTIP) Journal*, no 6, 1989

189 This relationship between diet and skin was discussed in a paper by R M B
MacKenna in *Research Review*, 1963–64, 'Dermatological Investigation'

CHAPTER 8

190 'Medicine and the Media, the road to disenchantment', *British Medical
Journal*, vol 305, 31 October 1992, p 1103

191 Lowry, Stella, 'What's wrong with medical education in Britain?' *British
Medical Journal*, vol 305, 21 November 1992, p 1279

192 'Europe looks at complementary medicine', *British Medical Journal*, vol 299,
4 November 1989, pp 1121, 1122

193 Reilly, David Taylor, 'Young doctors' views on alternative medicine', *British Medical Journal,* vol 287, 30 July 1983, p 337

194 'Germany looks at complementary medicine', *British Medical Journal,* vol 305, 5 December 1992, pp 1384, 1385

195 A professor is to be appointed to investigate claims by alternative medicines from a scientific point of view.

196 Kjeldsen-Kragh, J *et al,* 'Controlled trial of fasting and one-year vegetarian diet in rheumatoid arthritis', *The Lancet,* vol 338, no 8772, 12 October 1991, p 902

197 Deluze, C *et al,* 'Electroacupuncture in fibromyalgia: results of a controlled trial', *British Medical Journal,* vol 305, 21 November 1992, pp 1249, 1252

198 *Ibid,* p 1250

199 Twentyman, Ralph, *The Science and Art of Healing,* Floris Books, Edinburgh, 1989, pp 73,74

200 Leroi, A, 'Iscador therapy of cancer', *British Homoeopathic Journal,* vol LIV, no 1, January 1965, p 31

201 *Ibid,* p 27

202 Jeans, Sir James, *Physics & Philosophy,* Cambridge University Press, Cambridge 1942, p 171

203 *Ibid,* p 175

204 Report of the Board of Science Working Party on Alternative Therapy, *British Medical Journal,* vol 292, 24 May 1986, p 1407

205 Glymour, Clark, and Stalker, Douglas, 'Engineers, Cranks, Physicians, Magicians', *New England Journal of Medicine,* vol 308, no 16, pp 961, 962

206 *Ibid,* p 962

207 *Ibid,* p 962

208 Dixon, Bernard, *Beyond the Magic Bullet,* George Allen & Unwin, London, 1978, p 226

209 McKeown, Thomas, *The Role of Medicine, Dreams, Mirage, or Nemesis,* The Nuffield Provincial Hospital Trust, 1976, pp XIV

210 *Ibid,* p 14

211 *Ibid,* p 179

212 Sennett, Richard, 'Destructive Gemeinschaft' in *Beyond the Crisis,* ed Norman Birnbaum, Oxford University Press, New York, 1977, p 180

213 Ledermann, E K, 'Neglect of Mysteries in Medical Practice', *Explorations in Knowledge,* vol VIII, no 2, 1991

CHAPTER 9

214 Levinas, Emmanuel, 'Substitution', *The Levinas Reader,* Basil Blackwell, Oxford, 1989, pp 107, 108

215 Lingis, Alphonso, translator's Introduction to Emmanuel Levinas, *Collected Papers,* Martinus Nijhoff Publishers, 1987, p XIV

216 Wild, John, Introduction to Emmanuel Levinas, *Totality and Infinity, An Essay on Exteriority*, Kluwer Academic Publishers, 3rd printing, 1991, p 14

217 Levinas, Emmanuel, *Totality and Infinity*, Kluwer Academic Publishers, London, 1991, pp 51, 52

218 *Ibid*, pp 79, 80, 81

219 *Ibid*, p 43

220 *Ibid*, pp 76, 73

221 *Ibid*, p 79

222 *Ibid*, p 115

223 *Ibid*, p 133

224 *Ibid*, p 134

225 *Ibid*, p 142

226 *Ibid*, p 144

227 *Ibid*, p 155

228 *Ibid*, p 155

229 *Ibid*, pp 172–73

230 *Ibid*, p 178

231 *Ibid*, pp 202, 203

232 *Ibid*, pp 254, 255

233 *Ibid*, p 256

234 *Ibid*, p 266

235 *Ibid*, p 266

CHAPTER 10

236 van Deurzen-Smith, Emmy, *Existential Counselling in Practice*, Sage Publications, London, 1988, p 60

237 *Ibid*, pp 157–61

238 *Ibid*, p 162

239 *Ibid*, p 162

240 *Ibid*, p 160

241 *Ibid*, p 161

242 Robinson, Margaret, *Family transformation through divorce and remarriage, A systemic approach*, Routledge, London, 1991, p 40

243 Robinson, Margaret, *op cit* pp 207–209

244 *Ibid*, p 35

245 Robinson, Margaret, *op cit*, pp 207–209

CHAPTER 11

246 Foulkes, S H, *Therapeutic Group Analysis,* George Allen & Unwin, London, 1964

247 The present writer can vouch for this incident

248 Foulkes, S H, *op cit*, p 109

249 *Ibid*, pp 151, 152

250 *Ibid*, p 109

251 Foulkes, S H and Anthony, E J, *Group Psychotherapy, The Psycho-analytical Approach*, Pelican, Penguin Books, Harmondsworth, 2nd edn, 1965, p 26

252 Foulkes, S H, *op cit*, p 59

253 Foulkes, S H, *op cit*, p 141

254 Andrews, Gavin, 'The Essential Psychotherapies', *British Journal of Psychiatry*, no 162, 1993, pp 447–51

CHAPTER 12

255 Kelly, John C, *A Philosophy of Communication, Explorations for a Systematic Model*, The Centre for the Study of Communications and Culture, London, 1981, p 13

256 Cubitt, Terry, 'Crying out for succour', *British Medical Journal*, vol 306, 20 March 1993, p 800

257 *Ibid*, p 800

258 Wiener, Andrew, 'Problems on the other side of the fence', *British Medical Journal*, vol 306, 6 March 1993, p 661

259 Seedhouse, David, 'Exercise Three, Which Hat Should I Wear?', in *Liberating Medicine*, John Wiley & Sons, Chichester, 1991, pp 74–77

CHAPTER 13

260 *See* note 259

261 Seedhouse, David, *op cit*, p 147

262 *Ibid*, pp 4–17

263 *Ibid*, p 43

264 *Ibid*, p 44

265 *Ibid*, pp 45–51

266 *Ibid*, pp 90–92

267 *Ibid*, p 128

268 *Ibid*, pp 128,129

269 *Ibid*, p 135

270 *Ibid*, pp 123,124

271 *Ibid*, p 121

INDEX OF AUTHORS

———————————————• ———————————————

Adler, Alfred xii, 39–42, 59, 83
Andrews, Gavin 37–8
Anthony, E J 152
Atkins, Elisha 99

Bird, Howard 113
British Journal of Psychiatry 8
British Medical Journal 94, 96, 121–2,
    154–5
Buber, Martin, 4, 6, 57, 137–8

Cassirer, Ernst 58, 76
Chick, Jonathan 97
Collingwood, R G 83, 141

Dawkins, Richard 89–91
Descartes, René 26
Deutsch, Helene 152–3
Dewhurst, David 30
Dickson, Joan 114
Dixon, Bernard 128–9
Doctor 94–5

Fairbairn, W R O 33
Fenichel, Otto 35
Foulkes, S H 148, 150–1, 152, 153
Frankl, Viktor E 31
Freud, Sigmund 30–4, 37–8, 39, 59, 83,
    149–50, 151
Fromm, Erich 18, 138

Gautam, S 55
Glymour, Clark 126–7
Goethe, J W von 4, 36
GP 99

Hahnemann, Samuel 109
Hawkins, Anne 48
Heidegger, Martin 43–5, 54
Heinemann, Fritz 4–7
Holman, C 93
Hughes, Carol 9

Jaspers, Karl 4, 45–6, 135
Jeans, James 124–5
Jens 74
Jones, David 32
Jung, Carl xii, 35–6, 38, 59, 83

Kant, Immanuel 26, 108, 125
Kelly, John 154
Kielsden 174
Kierkegaard, Sören 82
King, Magda 43–4
Klein, Melanie 34–5, 59
Kohurt, Heinz 31
Kübler-Ross, Elizabeth 54–5

Lancet, The 174
Lavik, Nils Johan 15–16
Ledermann, E K 175
Levinas, Emmanuel 135–8, 139, 140,
    141–2, 151, 159, 162, 164, 165
Listener, The 10
Lowry, Stella 121

MacKay, Donald M 24–5
Mannheim, Karl 18–19, 43, 166
Marcel, Gabriel 26
McKeown, Thomas 128–9
Medical Research Council 9

Mims Magazine Weekly 9
Mitchell, Kevin 33
Moxham, J 95

New England Journal of Medicine 126–7
New Scientist 92, 128
Nijhawan, M 55
Nutrition and Health 94

Pastorelli, France 50–1, 52–3
Pavlov, Ivan 26
Pearson, Richard 113
Philip, Graham 9
Polanyi, Michael 31

Roberts, David E 82–4, 87, 130, 141
Robinson, Margaret 142
Rowe, Dorothy 47
Ryan, Cornelius 48–9, 52–3

Sargant, William 23
Sartre, Jean-Paul 7, 45, 83

Scheler, Max 46
Schultz, J H 107
Schweitzer, Albert 42
Seedhouse, David 157, 161–6
Sennett, Richard 19, 43, 45, 166
Simenon, Georges 51–2
Stalker, Douglas 126–7
Steiner, Rudolf 123–4
Straus, Erwin W 25–6, 125
Strupp, H H 33
Szasz, Thomas 13–14

Tillich, Paul 21
Trethowan, W H 23

van Deurzen-Smith, Emmy 139, 140
von Bertalanffy, Ludwig 20–1, 31, 43,
    166

Walters, A Harry 92
Weiss, Paul A 90–1
Woodger, J H 90–1

INDEX OF SUBJECTS

———————————— • ————————————

abortion 7
acupuncture xi, xii, 110, 119, 126
aggressiveness 33, 39, 68, 150–1
AIDS 16–18
air 92–9
alcohol 8, 15, 95–7
alternative medicine *see* holistic medicine
amphetamine 12
analgesics 12
angina pectoris 50–1, 53
Angry Boy (film) 58
anonymity 43–5
anthroposophical medicine 123–4, 126
art 20
    therapy 58–9, 144–6; pictures by
        patients 69, 70, 74, 75, 144–5;
        poems by patients 62–5
asthma 61, 87, 119, 126
    and autogenic training 115–16
attitudes, changing 28–9
authenticity 19–20, 43–5
    see also under self
autogenic training 107, 115–16
autonomy, patients' 163–6
    see also freedom, ethical
aversion therapy 27, 28

barbiturates 12
behaviour therapy 26–7
bereavement 48, 57, 120
body, wholeness 87–90
    biological 89–91
    machine-like 88–9, 125, 127
    medicine 125–30
    Natural Therapy 99–108

bowels 101, 102–3
    diarrhoea 107
brain
    diseases 22–4
    and mind 24–6, 125
breathing and breathlessness 42, 61, 101,
    115–16
    see also asthma

cancer
    challenge 48–9, 53, 87
    and diet 94
    and smoking 95
    treatment, iscador 123
children
    conscience 6
    development 33
    mental illness 8–9
    psychology 41–2
chiropractic 111–12
Christianity 82
cocaine 9
coffee 97–8
cognitive system 24–5
cognitive therapy 28–9
cola 98
communication 44, 154–6
conscience 3, 21, 24, 44
    corrected 67–8, 141–2
    ethics of 4–8
    and guilt 45–6, 47, 48
    as superego xii, 32–3, 149
counselling xii, 158
    existential 139–40
    scientific 140–2

death
  challenge 49, 54–6
  of mother 117
decision-making 24–5, 48
  see also freedom, ethical
dementia 22–3, 24
dependency on therapist 37
depression xii, 8, 47
  case histories 61–2, 73–6, 77–8, 144
  in children 9
  and conscience 5
  incidence 8
  treatment 116–19
desensitization 27–8
determinism 42, 43, 45
diarrhoea 107
diet and food xi, 102
  addictions 29, 102
  and disease 94
  holistic 100–1, 102, 118
  Natural Therapy 174
  processing 89
dietetics 88–9, 94, 100–1, 123
disease see illness
doctors
  relationships with patients 154–60,
    161
  training 121
Doctor's to Be (tv series) 121
Doll's House, A (Ibsen) 146
dream interpretations 34–5, 40–1, 59–60,
    78–9, 80, 146–8
drugs 8, 162
  addiction 8, 9–14, 40, 163;
    psychology 13–14; stages 11; and
    suicide 15
  psychotropic 23, 68, 83
  testing 88, 125, 128
  unnecessary medication 98–9

ecology 92–3
electroacupuncture 123
electrons 124–5
ethics 3–4, 162–4
  conflicts 7, 163
  of conscience 4–8
  existential 139–42

true-self xii–xiii, 33, 143, 162–3,
    165–6
  see also freedom, ethical
euthanasia 7
exercise 101, 104–7
existentialism 82–4, 87
  counselling 139–40

facelessness 73–6
families
  children in 41–2
  disorganization 14–15, 114
  withdrawal from 65–7, 70–1
  woman in 66–7
  see also marriage; mothers
Farewell to Childhood (film) 58
fasting 102, 123, 174
fatalism 42, 45
femininity 79–80
food see diet; dietetics
freedom, ethical xi, 3–4, 21, 24–5, 38,
    42, 44–5
  acceptance 48
  autonomy, patients' 163–6

genetics and heredity 87, 89–90
Germany
  alternative medicine 122–3
  autogenic training 107
Gestalt theory xii, 38–9, 83
group therapy
  psychoanalytic 149–53
  true-self xii, 80–1, 143–8
guilt 4, 5, 32, 45–7, 48, 68
  false xii, 47

hay fever 124, 128
health, maintaining 87–8, 100–2
heart disease 87, 100
Helsinki
  suicide 16
heredity and genetics 87, 89–90
heroin 9–10, 15, 163
holism xi–xii
  biological xii, 120, 122
holistic (alternative) medicine xi, 121–
    30, 162, 164–5

different nations' use 121–2
    research 122
homeopathy xi, xii, 108–10, 118–19,
    124, 126

illness
    challenge 48–54, 87–8, 89
    and conscience 5
    and food 94
    Natural Therapy 119–20
    treatment 164
    see also mental illness
inhalant drugs 11–12
International Society for the Study of
    Tension in Performance 113–14,
    75
iscador (mistletoe) 123

Japan
    suicide 15

kung fu 106

language 20, 137, 138
love 30–1, 89, 138, 139–40, 159
lung cancer 93, 95
lysergic acid diethylamide (LSD) 12–13

Madonna and Child, The (Epstein)
    58–9
marijuana 9
marriage 71–2, 73, 77–8
    counselling; existential 139–40;
        scientific 140–2
massage 111, 114, 119
meaninglessness ix, 20–1
mental illness xii, 5, 7–9, 20–1, 87
    see also depression
modelling behaviour 27
mothers
    death 117
    influence 74, 76, 77–8
    neglect 76, 77
    obligations to 7, 79
    Oedipus complex 5–6, 32
    reconciliation with 78–9
    surrogacy 7
multiple sclerosis 22–3, 24

muscular pain 113–15
    in asthma 116
musicians 113–15, 125

Natural Therapy xii, 92–112
    applications 101–7
    limitations 107–8
    principles 99–101
    treatments 113–20
neurophysiology 25
Norway
    suicide 15–16

Oedipus complex 5–6, 32
operant conditioning 27
organic psychiatry 22–4
Oslo, Norway 15–16
osteopathy 111
others 6–7, 135–8, 140

pictures by patients 69, 70, 74, 75, 76,
    77, 144–6
pleasure principle xii, 31–2, 78, 162
poems, by patients 62–5
pollution 92–3
posture 104, 105, 106
Preface to Life (film) 58
psyche-soma conundrum 24–6
psychiatry
    organic 22–4
psychoanalysis xii, 30–5, 141
    group treatment 149–53
psychology 5–6
    analytical 35–8
    individual 39–42
psychotherapy 31, 57–80
    dynamic 37–8, 152–3
    group xii, 80–1, 143–53;
        psychoanalytic 149–53
    true self 57–81; group 143–8

relationships
    counselling 139–42
    doctor-patient 154–60, 161
    with the Other 135–8, 140
    see also families; marriage; mothers
relaxation 106–7
    autogenic training 107, 115–16

religion 6, 82
reveries 60–1, 78
Roots of Happiness (film) 58

science 20, 24–5, 43
   in counselling 140–2
   medical xi, xii, 55, 89, 123–5,
      126–30, 162
   psychoanalytical 149–53
self
   authentic (true-) xii, 19–20, 21, 43–5,
      135–8, 163, 165–6
   assertion 61–73
   ethic xii, 48, 163, 165–6
   group treatment 80–1, 143–8;
      psychotherapy 57–81
   tests 48–56
   therapists 5–6, 33–4, 57–8, 60, 68,
      71–6, 77–8, 80, 163, 166;
      autonomy 163–6; and other 6–7,
      135–8
self-harm 16
senility 22
skin 101, 103–4
   irritation 116–19, 126
smoking xi, 94–5, 96, 97, 117, 118
soil 93, 100
spirituality 3–4
   challenges 43–56

spiritual existence 82–4
spiritual malaise 8–21
stroke 51–2, 53–4
suicide 14–16
   attempts, treatment of patients 157–8,
      161, 164

tai chi 106
tea 97–8
technology, medical 7, 121
therapists 21
   Natural 102, 107, 114, 115, 117–18
   true-self 5–6, 33–4, 163, 166; in case
      histories 68, 71–6, 77–8, 80;
      methods 57–8, 60
training, medical 121
tranquillizers 23–4
true-self *see* self, authentic

unconscious, collective 36

valuation 18–21, 166
vegetarianism 123

water 93
writing, by patients 61–7, 70–3

yoga 106–7, 114